LOUDER AN̶

P.G. Wodehouse was born in Guildford, Surrey, in 1881 and educated at Dulwich College. After working for the Hong Kong and Shanghai Bank for two years, he left to earn his living as a journalist and storywriter.

During his lifetime he wrote over ninety books, and his work has won worldwide acclaim. He was hailed by *The Times* as 'a comic genius recognized in his lifetime as a classic and an old master of farce'. P.G. Wodehouse said: 'I believe there are two ways of writing novels. One is mine, making a sort of musical comedy without music and ignoring real life altogether; the other is going right deep down into life and not caring a damn'.

In 1975 he was created a Knight of the British Empire and he died on St.Valentine's Day in the same year at the age of ninety-three.

BY P.G. WODEHOUSE
ALSO AVAILABLE IN VINTAGE

Aunts Aren't Gentlemen
Carry On Jeeves
The Code Of The Woosters
A Few Quick Ones
The Inimitable Jeeves
Jeeves And The Feudal Spirit
Jeeves In The Offing
Jeeves Takes Charge
Joy In The Morning
The Mating Season
Much Obliged, Jeeves
Nothing Serious
Right Ho, Jeeves
Stiff Upper Lip, Jeeves
Thank You, Jeeves
Very Good, Jeeves
The Clicking Of Cuthbert
Frozen Assets
Jill The Reckless
Meet Mr. Mulliner
Mr. Mulliner Speaking
Mulliner Nights
The Old Reliable
Something Fishy
The Heart Of The Goof
Plum Pie
Vintage Wodehouse
Ice In The Bedroom
The Coming Of Bill
The Girl In The Boat
Louder And Funnier
Bill The Conqueror
Barmy In Wonderland

P.G. Wodehouse

LOUDER AND FUNNIER

VINTAGE

Published by Vintage 1997

2 4 6 8 10 9 7 5 3 1

First published in Great Britain by
Faber and Faber Ltd., 1932

Vintage
Random House, 20 Vauxhall Bridge Road, London SW1V 2SA

Random House Australia (Pty) Limited
20 Alfred Street, Milsons Point, Sydney
New South Wales 2061, Australia

Random House New Zealand Limited
18 Poland Road, Glenfield,
Auckland 10, New Zealand

Random House South Africa (Pty) Limited
Endulini, 5A Jubilee Road, Parktown 2193, South Africa

Random House UK Limited Reg. No. 954009

A CIP catalogue record for this book
is available from the British Library

ISBN 0 09 982030 7

Papers used by Random House UK Ltd are natural, recyclable products made from wood grown in sustainable forests. The manufacturing processes conform to the environmental regulations of the country of origin

Printed and bound in Great Britain by
The Guernsey Press Co. Ltd., Guernsey, Channel Islands

To

George Blake

A Splendid Fellow
and
*Very Sound on Pekes**

*But he should guard against the tendency
to claim that his Peke fights Alsatians.
Mine is the only one that does this.

About this Book

I HAVE borrowed the title of this little volume of meditations from the old story (which, as they say, may be new to some of you present here to-night) of the nervous after-dinner speaker. Like so many of his species, he had begun his remarks in a faltering undertone, and he had not been in action long when the usual austere Voice said, "Louder, please." A few minutes later, another Voice went deeper into the matter.

"Louder, please," it observed, "*and* funnier."

There the story ends. One is left to suppose that the speaker did his best to oblige, as I have done.

Most of these essays were written originally more than a dozen years ago for the American magazine, *Vanity Fair*, at a time when the wolf at the door left little leisure for careful thought and the patient search for the *mot juste*. I had a wife, two cats, and a puppy to support, and my policy, in consequence, was to bung something down quick and cash in. You will all be glad to hear that I made quite a good thing out of it and was able to pay my bills with a promptitude which earned for me in the Long Island village where I was then living the nickname of Honest John.

But if you are writing for Posterity, as I am now, you cannot breeze along in this airy, slap-dash way. When Faber and Faber, the Russell Square twins, wanted a book of light essays and asked me if I had anything of the kind in my cellars, my immediate reply was "Boys, I've got a trunkful." I thought it would be simply a case of digging out the stuff, blowing the dust off it, and collecting the advance royalties. It was only when I came to examine the things that I realized my mistake.

To be fit reading for a cultivated British public, they had got to be louder and funnier. Not just a little louder and a little funnier, but much louder and much funnier. And to this end I have worked upon them like a beaver.

Always remember, therefore, that, much as you may dislike this book, it could have been considerably worse.

There are two drawbacks to writing a volume of this kind. One is that you can think, off-hand, of so many people who could have done it better. The other is that the essay form is a tricky one to handle. It is not as if you had a story to tell. Any one will listen to a story. What you are doing is just grabbing the reader by the slack of his coat and babbling to him, and all the time he is probably dying to get away and go about his business. "How long?" he is saying to himself, as he looks at his watch. "How long?" And when he does escape you can picture him telling everybody to be careful how they let you get hold of them, because the first thing they know you will be drooling. "Not a bad chap," he may say, if particularly charitable, "but I do wish he wouldn't try to be funny."

What I would really like would be to have this book judged in the indulgent spirit accorded to after-dinner speeches. I should like you all to use your imagination. Try to fancy that you are full to the brim with the *petite marmite*, the *poulet rôti*, the *sel d'agneau*, and that curious hair-oil ice-cream they serve at banquets; that you are flushed with heady wines; that you have undone the buttons of your waistcoat; and that your cigar is drawing well. Then all this will seem quite different.

As a matter of fact, it would be rather a good idea if you actually had a good, square meal before starting to tackle this book. Don't attempt to read it after breakfast or in the grey hours of the late afternoon. Hold back till you have dined. Then, with the coffee and old brandy at your side and within your soul that cosy feeling of being able to endure anything now, pitch in. You will be surprised what a difference it will make.

My publishers will support me in this. Faber *major* (with whom I do most of my business) tells me that they received the manuscript by an early post and that he and Faber *mi* could do literally nothing with it. They spent the day shoving it from one to the other, each trying to avoid the task of reading it. A clerk named Simmons was called in and ordered to have a go, but he resigned and is now coffee-planting in Kenya. The situation began to look like a deadlock, and then suddenly they got the idea that things might brighten after a good dinner.

What ensued? They dined as follows:

LE DÎNER

Hors d'œuvres variés

Consommé Julienne

Fried Smelts

Faisan Rôti

Soufflé au Maitre d'hôtel

Scotch Woodcock

washing it down with a *brut* champagne of a vintage year, and the next thing that happened was an ugly row because Faber *mi* got hold of the manuscript and refused to give it up, and Faber *ma* was so annoyed by his snorts and chuckles that he hit him over the head with a *croisson* or small French roll.

So, if you are hesitating about reading further, say to yourself "It can be done. The Fabers did it," and stoke up and go to it.

Contents

The Hollywood Scandal

EVERY one who is fond of authors—and, except for Pekingese, there are no domestic pets more affectionate and lovable —must have noticed how alarmingly scarce these little creatures have been getting of late. At one time London was full of them—too full, some people used to think. You would see them frisking in perfect masses in any editorial office you happened to enter. Their sharp, excited yapping was one of the features of the first- or second-act intermission of every new play that was produced. And in places like Chelsea and Bloomsbury you had to watch your step very carefully to avoid treading on them.

And now what do we see? Just an occasional isolated one being shooed out of a publisher's sanctum or sniffing at his press-clippings in a studio, and nothing more.

Run through the list for yourself. William Shakespeare ... has anyone seen Shakespeare lately? Percy (Skylark) Shelley ... what has become of Percy? And Dickens, Thackeray, Trollope, Martin Tupper, the poet Bunn ... where are they? They have simply disappeared.

Time after time I have had fanciers come up to me with hard-luck stories.

"You know that novelist of mine with the flapping ears and the mass of spots on his coat?" says one. "Well, he's gone."

"Gone?"

"Absolutely vanished. I left him on the steps of the club, and when I came out there were no signs of him."

"Same here," says another. "I had a brace of playwrights

13

to whom I was greatly attached, and they've disappeared without a word."

Well, of course, we took it for granted that they had strayed and had got run over, for authors are notoriously dreamy in traffic and, however carefully you train them, will persist in stopping in the middle of the street to jot down strong bits of dialogue. It is only very recently that the truth has come out.

They are all in Hollywood, making Talking Pictures.

With the advent of the Talkies, as might have been expected, radical changes have taken place in Hollywood. The manufacture of motion pictures has become an infinitely more complex affair. You know how it was in the old days. Informal. Casual. Just a lot of great big happy schoolboys getting together for a bit of fun. Ike would have a strip of celluloid, Spike a camera that his uncle had given him for Christmas, Mike would know a friend or two who liked dressing up and having their photographs taken, and with these modest assets they would club together their pocket-money and start the Finer and Supremer Films Corporation. And, as for bothering about any one to write them a story, it simply never occurred to them. They just made it up among themselves as they went along.

That old, simple era has passed. Nowadays you can't just put on a toga, press a button, and call the result The Grandeur That Was Rome or In The Days Of Nero. A whole elaborate new organization is required. You have to have a Chief Executive to superintend the Producer, a Producer to superintend the Supervisor, a Supervisor to supervise the sub-Supervisor, a sub-Supervisor to sub-supervise the Director, a Director to direct the Camera-man, and an Assistant Director to assist the Director. You have to surround yourself with highly trained specialists,—one to put in the lisps, another to get the adenoid effects, a third to arrange the catarrh. And, above all, you must get hold of authors to supply the words.

The result has been one of the gravest scandals that have ever afflicted the body politic. And, to correct this scandal, it is time that some fearless square-shooter stepped forward and spoke in no uncertain voice.

Please do not minimize the gravity of the situation. Do not shrug it away in a spirit of easy philosophy with some such remark as "Oh, there are always bound to be plenty of authors" or "If one is missing there'll be another along in a minute". I warn England that, unless steps are taken, there will soon be a very serious shortage. And then who will write you your Sunday-paper articles on The Modern Girl or The Decay of Home-Life? Suppose you reached out for Dean Inge one morning and he wasn't there? That makes you think, doesn't it?

Absurd, you say? Only dynamite could get Dean Inge away from the *Evening Standard*? Don't be too sure. Matters have reached such a pitch that you cannot be certain of anybody nowadays. Do you realize that all that year I was away from London, when everybody supposed that I was doing a short stretch at Dartmoor, I was actually in Hollywood? And that if I had not bribed the gaoler's daughter to smuggle in a file in a meat-pie, I should be there still? Very well, then.

Hollywood is a terribly demoralizing place The whole atmosphere there is one of insidious deceit and subterfuge. Nothing is what it affects to be. What looks like a tree is really a slab of wood backed with barrels. What appears on the screen as the towering palace of Haroun-al-Raschid is actually a cardboard model occupying four feet by three of space. The languorous lagoon is simply a smelly tank with a stage-hand named Ed. wading about in it in a bathing-suit.

Imagine the effect of all this on a sensitive-minded author. Taught at his mother's knee to love the truth, he finds himself surrounded by people making fortunes by what can only be called chicanery. He begins to wonder whether mother had the right idea. After a month or two in such an environment could you trust that author to count his golf shots correctly or to give his right circulation figures?

And then there is the inevitable sapping of his self-respect. Authors in Hollywood are kept in little hutches. In every studio there are rows and rows of these, each containing an author on a long contract at a weekly salary. You see their anxious little faces peering out through the bars. You hear them whining piteously to be taken for a walk. And does the heart bleed? You bet it bleeds. One has to be very callous not to be touched by such a spectacle.

After all, authors are people. They are entitled to life, liberty, and the pursuit of happiness. It cannot be right to keep them on the chain. Surely some sort of an honour system would be possible.

I do not say that all these authors, or, indeed, a majority of them, are actually badly treated. Indeed, in the best studios kindness is the rule. Often you will see Mr. Warner or Mr. Lasky stop and give one of them a lettuce. And the same may be said of the humaner type of director.

In fact, between the directors and these authors there frequently exists a rather touching friendship. I remember Mr. King Vidor telling me a story that illustrates this. One morning, it seems, he was on his way to his office, preoccupied, as is his habit when planning out the day's work, when he felt a sudden tug at his coat-tails. He looked down and there was his pet author, William Edgar ("Strikes a New Note") Delamere. The little fellow had got him in a firm grip and was gazing up at him, in his eyes an expression of dumb warning.

Well, Mr. Vidor, not unnaturally, mistook this at first for mere playfulness, for he had often romped with his little charges. Then—he does not know why—something seemed to whisper to him that he was being withheld from some great peril. He remembered stories he had read as a boy—one of which he was even then directing for Rin-Tin-Tin—where faithful dogs dragged their masters back from the brink of precipices on dark nights.

Scarcely knowing why, he turned and went off to the *cafeteria* and had a small malted milk. And it was as well that he did. In his office, waiting to spring, there was lurking a foreign star with a bad case of temperament, whose bite might have been fatal. You may be sure that William Edgar had a good meal that night.

But that is an isolated case. Not all directors are like Mr. Vidor. Too many of them crush the spirit of the captive by incessant blue-pencilling of their dialogue so that they become listless and lose ambition and appetite. Neglect is what kills an author. Cut his stuff too much, make him feel that he is not a Voice, give him the impression that you think his big scene all wet, and you will soon see the roses fade from his cheeks.

They tell me there are authors who have been on salary for years at Hollywood without ever having a line of their work used. All they do is attend story conferences. There are other authors on some of the lots whom nobody has seen for years. It is like the Bastille. They just sit in some hutch away in a corner somewhere and grow grey beards and languish. From time to time somebody renews their contract, and then they are forgotten again.

Conditions being as I have described, it may be asked:

Why do authors go to Hollywood? The answer can be given in a single word—Coercion.

In fairness to the motion-picture magnates, I must admit that they very seldom employ actual physical violence. Occasionally a more than ordinarily obdurate author will be sandbagged in a dark alley and shipped across the Mojave Desert in an unconscious condition, but as a general rule the system is more subtle.

What generally happens is this. A couple of great film barons—say, Mr. Lasky and Mr. Zukor—will sight their quarry in the street and track him down to some Bohemian eating resort. Having watched him settle, they seat themselves at a table immediately behind him.

For a few moments there is silence, broken only by the sound of the author eating celery. Then Mr. Lasky addresses Mr. Zukor, raising his voice slightly.

"Whatever was the name of that girl?" he says, meditatively.

"What girl?" asks Mr. Zukor, taking his cue.

"That tall, blonde girl."

"What tall, blonde girl?"

"The one in the pink bathing-suit at that Beach Club party."

"You mean the one with the freckle in the small of the back?"

"A freckle? A mole, I always understood."

"No, a freckle. Just over the base of the spinal cord."

"Well, be that as it may, what was her name?"

"I forget. I'll ask her when we get back. I know her intimately."

Here they pause, but not for long. There is a sound of quick, emotional breathing. The author is standing beside them, a rapt expression on his face.

"Pardon me, gentlemen," he says, "for interrupting what was intended to be a private conversation, but I fancy I overheard you saying that you were intimately acquainted with a tall, blonde girl in the habit of wearing bathing-suits of just the type I like best. It is for a girl of that description, oddly enough, that I have been scouring the country for years. Where may she be found?"

"In God's Back-Garden—Hollywood," says Mr. Lasky.

"Pity you can't meet her," says Mr. Zukor.

"If you were by any chance an author," says Mr. Lasky, "we could take you back with us to-morrow."

"Prepare yourselves for a surprise, gentlemen," says the victim. "I *am* an author. J. Montague Breamworthy. His powerfully devised situations—*N.Y. Times*. Sheer, stark realism—*Herald-Tribune*. Not a dull page—*Women's Wear*."

"In that case," says Mr. Lasky, producing a contract, "sign here."

"Where my thumb is," says Mr. Zukor.

The trap has snapped.

When this plan fails, sterner methods are employed. The demand for authors at Hollywood has led to the revival of the old press-gang. Competition between the studios has become so keen that nowadays no one is safe even if he merely looks like an author.

I heard of one very interesting case. It appears that there was a man who had gone out West hoping to locate oil. He was, indeed, one of those men without a thought in the world outside of oil. The last thing he had ever dreamed of doing was to be an author. With the exception of letters and an occasional telegram of greeting to some relative at Christmas he had never written anything in his life.

But, by some curious chance, it happened that his appear-

ance was that of one capable of the highest feats in the way
of dialogue. He had a domelike head, piercing eyes, and that
rather cynical twist of the upper lip which generally means
an epigram on the way.

Still, as I say, he was not a writer, and no one was more
surprised than himself when, walking along a deserted street
in Los Angeles, thinking of oil, he was suddenly set upon
by masked men, chloroformed, and whisked away in a closed
car. When he came to himself he was in a hutch on the Fox
lot with a pad and a sharpened pencil before him, and stern-
featured men were telling him to get busy and turn out
something with lots of sex in it, but not too much, because
of Will Hays.

The story has a curious sequel. A philosopher at heart,
he accepted the situation. He wrenched his mind away from
oil and scribbled a few sentences that happened to come into
his mind. He found, as so many have found, that an author's
is the easiest job in existence, and soon he was scratching
away as merrily as the oldest and highest-browed inhabitant.
And that is how Noel Coward got his start.

But not every kidnapped author accepts his fate so equably.
The majority endeavour to escape. But it is useless. Even if
the rigours of the pitiless California climate do not drive
them back to shelter, capture is certain, for the motion-picture
magnates stick at nothing.

When I was in Hollywood there was much indignation
among the better element of the community over the pursuit
of one unfortunate whom the harshness of his director, a man
of the name of Legree, had driven to desperation. He ran
away, and, if I got the story correctly, they chased him across
the ice with bloodhounds.

The whole affair was very unpleasant and has shocked the soft-hearted greatly. So much so that a Mrs. Harriet B. Stowe, of 3410, Sunset-avenue and Beverly, told me that if she could fix up the movie end with Metro-Goldwyn she intended to write a book about it which would stir the world.

"Boy," she said to me, "it will be a scorcher!"

And there the matter rests.

Such are the facts. As to what is to be done about it I confess I am a little vague. I can only recommend author-fanciers to exercise from now on incessant vigilance. When you take your pet for a walk, keep an eye on him. If he goes sniffing after strange men, whistle him back.

And remember that the spring is the dangerous time. In the spring authors get restless and start dreaming about bathing-parties. It is easy to detect the symptoms. The moment yours begins muttering about the Golden West and God's Sunshine and Out There Beyond the Stifling City put sulphur in his absinthe and lock him up in the kitchenette.

Literature and the Arts

1. To the Editor—Sir . . .

SUCCESS comes to a writer, as a rule, so gradually that it is always something of a shock to him to look back and realize the heights to which he has climbed. I know this was so in my own case. Editors to-day jump at my work and people have been saying nice things about it for years, but it never occurred to me that I was anywhere near the head of my profession till the other morning when Mother Of Five (Peckham) met me in the club and, pointing to a letter of mine in the *Daily Mirror* on Friendship And The Modern Girl, said there wasn't another man in England who could have done it. He exaggerated, of course, but it did bring home to me how far I had climbed since that distant summer when, an eager lad in my teens, I first came to London and started trying to contribute to the Correspondence Columns of the daily papers.

It gives me a curious feeling, half proud, half wistful, to think of those days of struggle, when it seemed so impossible that I should ever find an editor who believed in me. How I used to envy the men who had arrived—Paterfamilias, Disgusted Liberal, and the rest of them. Giants they seemed to me then. I can still recall the thrill that choked me when dear old Two Working-Girls (Brondesbury) gave me my first word of encouragement.

"Stick to it!" he said, wagging his grey beard. (I had been showing him some of my rejected work.) "You have the fire, the enthusiasm. All you need is to persevere. For never forget, my boy, that there is no royal road to success. I was six years getting my first letter printed, and even then they cut it down to three lines."

And he drained his mug of beer and went on with what he was writing. It was, I recollect, that noble passage which begins:

To the Editor, "Daily Express".
"Sir,—
"A curious fact which few have realized in connexion with the Albert Hall . . ."

You know it, of course. It is in the collected edition of his works. Many good critics consider that he never did anything finer.

We are a proud guild, we writers of letters to the papers. We hold our heads high and are a little apt to look down on other forms of authorship. Nor, I think, without reason. I always remember Indignant Householder uttering a dictum which crystallizes our attitude. "Novelists", he said, "are merely those who have failed as contributors to the Correspondence Column." What he meant was that every author really wants to have letters printed in the papers. Unable to make the grade, he drops down a rung of the ladder and writes novels.

To test the truth of this, ask the man who has done both. Ask Galsworthy, for instance, what it felt like to see the Forsyte Saga in print. He yawns. But just mention that you were reading that letter of his in the Sussex Farmer's Intelligencer (with which is incorporated The Wheat-Grower's Gazette and East Grinstead Mangold-wurzel) about the disgraceful condition of the footpath leading to the Baptist Chapel, and watch his face light up. The truth is that a novel, after all, is rather a commercial sort of affair. A letter to the papers is Art for Art's sake.

If I were giving advice to a youngster trying to make good in this most exacting of all branches of literature, I would say: "Write plainly on one side of the paper only. Condense your ideas. Be prepared for rebuffs. And, finally, do not try to run before you can walk. In other words, start—as we all have started—with the cuckoo."

Nobody knows why, but editors have a weak spot for cuckoos, and any one who hears the first one is pretty sure of an entrée to their columns. The only trouble is that what is known in my profession as "cuckoo-work" is not so simple as it looks. It calls for the most precise timing. If you don't get your letter in early enough, some rival forestalls you, and there is, oddly enough, no market whatever for the second man who hears the cuckoo. On the other hand, if you get it in too early, it becomes merely silly. I mean, it is no use writing to the *Daily Mail* on January the First and saying "Sir,—A very happy and prosperous New Year to you and all your readers. In this connexion, it may be of interest that at 11.45 last night I distinctly heard the cuckoo. . . ." The editor simply laughs, and not a nice laugh, either.

Still, the only thing is to keep trying, and I say once more, "Start with the cuckoo". And be careful that it is a cuckoo. D. B. Wyndham Lewis has told us that he once wrote to his daily paper saying that he had heard the first chaffinch, and the letter was suppressed because it clashed with certain powerful vested interests.

Another piece of advice I would give is this. Watch yourself closely. Take care that the letter-writing urge does not grow upon you till it becomes a vice. You may say you can take it or leave it alone, but can you? Be very sure that you are not like the tiger-cub who, in its infancy satisfied with bananas, is a changed animal the moment it has tasted blood and swallowed its first coolie. In my own case, I am sorry to say, my character has deteriorated very noticeably as the result of my life work. As a young man, I was mild and unassuming. To-day, I want to spend the whole of my time putting everybody right. I cannot see the simplest statement in print without seizing pen and paper and contradicting it— often with the greatest acerbity—in a letter beginning "Sir,— In your yesterday's issue you made the astounding assertion that . . ."

And in saying that I have given myself away. I have revealed that I am one of those letter-writers who require a peg on which to hang their efforts. In other words, successful though I am, I am not really one of the big men. I have never got quite to the top. The noblest writers of letters to the daily papers are those who burst forth spontaneously, like a lark breaking into song.

"Sir,—

"I wonder how many of your readers are aware that an excellent lotion for the hair may be made of crushed prunes and salad-oil. . . ."

or

"Sir,—

"My mother, who was the seventh daughter of a seventh daughter, married my father, who was the seventh son of a seventh son, in 1877. I am their seventh child, and was born on the seventh of July at seven in the morning. I am forty-seven round the waist and have seven Siamese cats. . . ."

Practically all a lesser man can do when he comes across

this sort of thing is to bow his head and say "Hail to thee, blithe spirit!" and let it go at that.

Another proof that I am not one of the real top-notchers, like Amazed and Old-Fashioned (to name but two), is that I have written this—out of lust for gold—as an article. As it is an article, I shall get paid for it. But Amazed would not have been swayed by a consideration like that. Nor would Old-Fashioned, nor Late Colonel, R.E. They would have put a "Sir" in front of it, and sent it to one of the daily papers as a letter.

2. *My Gentle Readers*

I HAVE often felt a little sorry for writers like Cicero or Diogenes Laertius, or, for the matter of that, Pliny the Elder, who operated in the days before the post office came into existence. They could never tell for certain when they had pushed their stuff across and made a solid hit with the great public. For, as everybody knows, an author's success can be estimated by the number of letters he receives from readers. It is the acid test.

Pliny, of course, had a few old school friends who thought he was a wonder—or, at any rate, told him so when they had made quite sure that he was going to pay for the last round of Falernian wine; and sometimes a kindly Senator would pat Cicero on the shoulder in the Campus Martius and say, "Stick at it, boy. You're doing fine!" But, looking at the thing in a broad way, they were simply working in the dark, and it must have been discouraging for them.

There is no point on which your modern author is more touchy than this business of testimonials from the public. You will see Galsworthy stroll up to Kipling in the club and yawn with an ill-assumed carelessness.

"You don't happen to know of a good secretary, do you, Rud?" he says. "I have been caught short, confound it. Mine has just got typist's cramp, answering letters from admirers of my books, and more pouring in by every post."

"John," says Kipling, "you know me. If I could help you, I would do it like a shot. But I'm in just the same fix myself. Both my secretaries collapsed this morning and are in hospital with ice-packs on their heads. I've never known the fan-mail heavier."

"Look here," says Galsworthy, abruptly, "how many fan-letters did you get last week?"

"How many did you?" says Kipling.

"I asked you first," says Galsworthy, and they parted on bad terms.

And, over in a corner, Hugh Walpole rising and walking away in a marked manner from H. G. Wells.

As far as I, personally, am concerned, if I am to submit to this test, I should describe myself as a sort of fair-to-medium—not, on the one hand, a definite wam, and yet not, on the other, a total bust. Something about half-way in between. The books which I write seem to appeal to a rather specialized public. Invalids like me. So do convicts. And I am all right with the dog-stealers. As regards Obuasie, I am not so sure.

From Obuasie (wherever that is) there arrived a short while ago the following letter, rather flatteringly addressed to "P. G. Wodehouse, England":

"Dear Sir,—

"I have heard your name and address highly have been recommended to me by a certain friend of mine that you are the best merchant in your city London. So I want you to

send me one of your best catalogue and I am ready to deal
with you until I shall go into the grave.

"Soon as possible send me early.

"I remain,

"Yours very good trully."

Now, it is difficult to know just what to make of a letter
like that. At first glance, of course, it would seem as if the
old boy had clicked in Obuasie on rather an impressive scale.
But there is also the possibility that some mistake or confusion has arisen. If I get my publishers to flood Obuasie
with my books, will they command a ready sale, or is Obuasie
under the impression that I deal in something quite different
from veritable masterpieces of absorbing fiction? Misunder-
standings so easily occur at a distance. You remember the
story of the traveller in cement docks, who would often rush
half-way across the world on hearing that there was a demand
for his wares in Pernambuco or Spitzbergen, only to discover,
after he had dragged his bag of samples all that weary way,
that what the natives really wanted was not docks but socks.

Better, perhaps, then, for the moment, to give Obuasie a
miss and stick to the invalids and convicts, who, with the
dog-stealers, surely make up a public quite large enough for
any author who is not utterly obsessed by the lust for gold.

My popularity with invalids puts me in something of a
quandary. Naturally, I like my stories to be read as widely
as possible; but, kind-hearted by nature, I do not feel altogether happy when I think that some form of wasting sickness is an essential preliminary to their perusal. And such
seems to be the case.

I can understand it, of course. You know how it is. When
you are fit and strong and full of yeast and all that sort of
thing, you go about with your chin up and your chest out,

without a single morbid tendency. "I feel great," you say, "so why should I deliberately take the sunshine out of life by reading Wodehouse?" And you don't.

So far, so good. But comes a day when the temperature begins to mount, the tonsils to ache, and dark spots to float before the eyes. Then, somehow or other, you find one of my books by your bedside, and a week later you are writing me to the following effect:

"Dear Sir,—

"I have never read anything of yours before, as I have always enjoyed robust health from a boy. But recently, owing to drinking unfiltered water, I became covered with pink spots and my brain-power was temporarily affected. A friend lent me your latest story, and I read it with great enjoyment. Kindly send me your photograph and autographed copies of all your other books.

     "Thanking you in anticipation,
       "I remain,
          "Yours truly."

You see the dilemma this places me in? On the one hand, I am rejoiced that the sufferer is now convalescent. On the other, I feel that until he contracts some other ailment I have lost a reader. If you want to see a mind in a ferment of doubt and indecision, take a look at mine when the papers announce that another epidemic has broken out and hundreds collapsing daily.

But, you will say, why bother about the invalids if the heart of the dog-stealers remains sound? And here I am faced by a somewhat embarrassing confession. When I said I was read by dog-stealers I was swanking. It is not dog-stealers who enjoy my work, but a (one) solitary dog-stealer, and—a galling thought—a rotten dog-stealer, at that, for he specifically admits to having been arrested. And, further, his motives in writing to me are mixed. It was not simply a clean, flame-like admiration for a great artist that caused him to take pen in hand, but also a desire to know whether I would give him a sum of money sufficient to enable him to start a street bookmaker's business. In fact, the more I think over this letter, the less confident do I feel that the man is going to be anything in the nature of a steady income to me down the long years.

One has got to face facts. The way I figure it out is that in order to buy my books he is obliged to steal dogs, and in order to steal dogs in anything like the necessary quantity he will have to develop considerably more skill than he possesses at present. As a commercial proposition, therefore, I can only write him down as shaky. He might have a good year, when the dogs came briskly in and he felt himself in a position not only to buy his own copy but to send others as birthday presents to his friends. But the chances are far greater that his bungling methods will lead to another arrest, and what use will he be to me, shut off from the book-stores just at the moment when my new novel needs support to make it go?

For he is a London dog-stealer, and in English prisons they tend to give the inmate nothing to read but things like the first volume of *Waverley* and *Marvels of Pond Life*. My convict public is entirely American. I have had so many letters recently from American penitentiaries that I am beginning to think that the American criminal must look on one or more of my works as an essential part of his kit.

I seem to see the burglar's mother sending him off for the night shift.

"Another cup of cocoa, Clarence?"

"No, thank you, mother. I must be off."

"Yes, it is getting late. Are you well wrapped up?"

"Yes, mother."

"Wearing your warm underclothing?"

"Yes, mother."

"Have you everything you need? Revolver? Brass knucks? Oxyacetylene blow-pipe? Wodehouse novel? Black jack? Skeleton keys? Mask?"

"Yes, mother."

"Then Heaven speed you, boy, and always remember what your dear father used to say: Tread lightly, read your Wodehouse, and don't fire till you see the whites of their eyes."

There was a gunman in Chicago last year who, in a fit of preoccupation caused by business worries, imprudently took with him by mistake a copy of Harold Bell Wright. The shock of discovering his blunder, when he opened the volume to go on with Chapter Eleven, so unnerved him that he missed the policeman at three yards and was expelled from his gang in disgrace. He was formally stripped of his machine-gun at the next general meeting, and is now a soda-jerker in a small town in Kansas.

You cannot be too careful if you wish to succeed in a difficult and overcrowded profession.

Yes, I go like a breeze in the prisons of America: and, as I say, I am much read by those whose minds have been temporarily unhinged by physical suffering. And yet, at the risk of seeming ungracious, I must own that I am not entirely satisfied. Apart from the uncomfortable thought that the study of my books may be a part of an American prison-sentence, I cannot restrain a wistful yearning for a few readers of sound health who do not belong to the criminal classes. It is nice, of course, to be looked on as a valuable counter-irritant in cases of mumps, measles, or tertiary fever. And it is pleasant to feel that the tedium of drilling a safe has been mitigated for many a conscientious workman by an occasional glance at a story of mine.

Nevertheless, I do have this yearning: and it would be a great pleasure to me if I could somehow manage to interest a few blameless and robust persons in my books.

I thought I had found one the other day. She sat next to me at dinner, one of those delightful, intelligent old ladies from whom the years have not taken their keenness of mind and their ability to spot a good man when they see one.

"This is a great moment for me," she said. "I can't tell you how proud I am. I think I have read everything you have ever written."

I looked at her closely. Her features were not worn with suffering. If there had been an Old Ladies' Marathon event at the Olympic Games, I would have expected to see her win it in a canter.

"Had much sickness in your family lately?" I asked, to make sure.

"None," she said. "We are an extraordinarily healthy family. We all love your books. My eldest son reads nothing else. He is in America now."

This sounded suspicious.

"Joliet?" I said. "Or Sing-Sing?"

"He is at the Embassy in Washington."

"Has *he* been pretty fit lately?"

"He is never ill."

"And he reads my books?"

"Every one of them. And so do my grandsons. The table in their room is piled with them. And when I go home to-night", she added, "and tell them that I have actually been sitting at dinner next to Edgar Wallace, I don't know what they will say!"

3. *Thrillers*

IT is an odd fact, frequently commented upon by thoughtful observers, that most of the great plagues in history have crept upon the world insidiously and without warning. Nobody notices that anything in particular is happening until one day the populace wakes up to find the trouble full-blown in its midst.

In the Middle Ages, for instance, everything was perfectly peaceful and normal—knights jousting, swineherds herding swine, landowners busy with soc and seisin and all that sort of thing—when one morning—on a Tuesday it was, six weeks come Lammas Eve—a varlet, strolling along the road between Southampton and Winchester (where the filling-station is now), encountered a malapert knave and fell into conversation with him after the sociable habit of those days.

"How now?" quoth the varlet.

"Ye same to you," said the knave, courteously.

After which, as usually happens when two sons of the soil get together for a chat, there was a pause of about twenty minutes. At the end of this period the varlet spoke.

"In my village there has chanced a happening", he said, "which hath caused much marvel. Rummy, is ye general verdict. Old Bill of ye Mill suddenly turned black yesterday."

"Black?" said the knave, wondering.

"Black is right."

"Well, by St. James of Compostella, if that doth not beat ye band!" exclaimed the knave. "Down where I live, George ye Cowherd hath turned black, too."

"Thou dost not say!"

"Of a verity I do say."

"What can have caused this?" cried the varlet.

"I could not tell thee," said the knave. "I am a stranger in these parts myself."

And a week later the Black Death was all over the country, and a man who did not look like Al Jolson singing "Sonny Boy" could scarcely be found anywhere.

In much the same way, quietly and, as it were, surreptitiously, the present flood of Mystery Thrillers has engulfed the British Isles. Only a short while ago the evil appeared merely sporadic. Now we are up to our necks in the things and more coming all the time. There seems to be some virus in the human system just now which causes the best of writers to turn out thrillers. This would not matter so much, only, unfortunately, it causes the worst of writers to turn them out, too.

The result is that this royal throne of kings, this sceptred isle, this earth of majesty, this seat of Mars, this other Eden, demi-Paradise, this fortress built by Nature for herself against infection and the hand of war, this happy breed of men, this little world, this precious stone set in the silver sea, which serves it in the office of a wall or as the moat defensive of a house . . . well, to cut a long story short, England . . . has degenerated into an asylum full of patients reading each other's mystery stories. And ninety-nine out of every hundred a dud.

A disquieting thought.

And the worst of it is that ninety-six out of every hundred contain a heroine and a love-story.

Who ever first got the idea that any one wants a beastly girl messing about and getting in the way when the automatics are popping I am at a loss to imagine. Nobody has a greater respect than myself for girls in their proper place—in the paddock at Ascot, fine: at Lord's during the luncheon interval of the Eton and Harrow match, capital: if I went to a night-club and found no girls there, I should be the first to complain: but what I do say is that they have no business in Lascar Joe's Underground Den at Limehouse on a busy evening. Apart from anything else, Woman seems to me to lose her queenly dignity when she is being shoved into cupboards with a bag over her head. And, if there is one thing certain, it is that sooner or later something of that sort will be happening to the heroine of a thriller.

For, though beautiful, with large grey eyes and hair the colour of ripe corn, the heroine of the thriller is almost never a very intelligent girl. Indeed, it would scarcely be overstating it to say her mentality is that of a cockroach—and not an ordinary cockroach, at that, but one which has been dropped on its head as a baby. She may have escaped death a dozen times. She may know perfectly well that the notorious Blackbird Gang is after her to secure the papers. The police may have warned her on no account to stir outside her house. But when a messenger calls at half-past two in the morning with an unsigned note saying "Come at once", she just snatches at her hat and goes. The messenger is a one-eyed Chinaman with a pock-marked face and an evil grin, so she trusts him immediately and, having accompanied him to the closed car with steel shutters over the windows, bowls off in it to the ruined cottage in the swamp. And when the hero, at great risk and inconvenience to himself, comes to rescue her, she will have nothing to do with him because she has been told by a mulatto with half a nose that it was he who murdered her brother Jim.

This girl must go. We readers demand it. We know the publishers want a female in the story so that they can put her on the jacket with her hands clasped and a wild look of agony in her eyes, but nevertheless we stick to it that she must go. Better a jacket with only a masked man pushing a paper-knife into a millionaire in his library than this continued poisoning of sensational fiction with imbeciles like Myrtle or Gladys or Elaine or whatever her name may be.

What we all liked so much about Sherlock Holmes was his correct attitude in this matter of girls in mystery stories. True, he would sometimes permit them to call at Baker Street and tell him about the odd behaviour of their uncles or step-fathers ... in a pinch he might even allow them to marry Watson ... but once the story was under way they had to retire into the background and stay there. That was the spirit, and we want a little more of it nowadays.

The obvious person, of course, to rid us of these pests is the villain, and in fairness to a willing worker it cannot be denied that he does his best. He has the zeal, the enthusiasm—every quality, you would say, which is required for the task. And yet, for one reason or another, he always fails. Even when he has got the girl chained up in the cellar under the wharf with the water pouring through the grating we never in our hearts really expect the happy ending. Experience has taught us that we cannot rely on this man. He has let us down too often, and forfeited our confidence. We know him for what he is, a broken reed.

Broadly speaking, the trouble with every villain of a thriller is that he suffers from a fatal excess of ingenuity. When he was a boy, his parents must thoughtlessly have told him that he was clever, and it has absolutely spoiled him for effective work.

The ordinary man, when circumstances compel him to murder a female acquaintance, borrows a revolver and a few cartridges and does the thing in some odd five minutes of the day when he is not at the office or the pictures. He does not bother about art or technique or scientific methods. He just goes and does it.

But the villain cannot understand simplicity. A hundred times he manœuvres the girl into a position where one good dig with a knife or a carefully directed pistol-shot would produce the happiest results, and then, poor ass, he goes and ruins it all by being too clever. It never occurs to him just to point a pistol at the heroine and fire it. If you told him the thing could be done that way, he would suspect you of pulling his leg. The only method he can imagine is to tie her in a chair, erect a tripod, place the revolver on it, tie a string to the trigger, pass the string along the walls till it rests on a hook, attach another string to it, pass this over a hook, tie a brick to the end of the second string and light a candle under it. He has got the thing reasoned out. The candle will burn the second string, the brick will fall, the weight will tighten the first string, thus pulling the trigger, and there you are.

Then somebody comes along and blows the candle out, and all the weary work to do over again.

Still, I suppose it is no use being angry with the poor fellows. They are doing their best according to their lights. It is simply that they are trying to tackle a highly specialized job without the requisite training. What the villain needs is to forget all he thinks he knows and go right back to the beginning and start learning the business from the bottom up. He requires careful schooling. And this is what he ought to be given at once if thrillers are to be purged of heroines.

The keynote of the curriculum of this School for Villains would be the inculcation of simplicity and directness. The pupil would receive at first what one might call a kindergarten education. For the greater part of his opening term he would confine himself to swatting flies. From this he

would work up through the animal kingdom in easy stages
till eventually he arrived at heroines. By the time he had
taken his degree, the Myrtles and Gladyses would be climbing
trees and pulling them up after them to avoid the man, for
by then he would be really dangerous.

The great difficulty, of course, would be to restrain and
hold in check that infernal ingenuity of his. The average
villain's natural impulse, if called upon to kill a fly, would
be to saw away the supports of the floor, tie a string across
the doorway, and then send the fly an anonymous letter
urging it to come at once in order to hear of something to
its advantage. The idea being that it would hurry to the
room, trip over the string, fall on the floor, tumble into the
depths, and break its neck.

That, to the villain's mind, is not merely the simplest, it
is the only way of killing flies. And the hardest task facing
his form-master would be to persuade him that excellent
results may be obtained through the medium of a rolled-up
Daily Mail gripped by the Football Coupon.

The maddening thing is that it is only when dealing with
the heroine that he is so beastly clever. With anybody of his
own sex he can be as straightforward as a medieval headsman.
Give him a baronet and he will stick a knife in his back
without a second thought. But the moment he finds himself
up against a heroine he seems to go all to pieces, and we
get all this stuff of suspending snakes from the chandelier
and fooling about with bombs which can only be exploded
by means of a gramophone record with an A in alt on it.

I have known a villain to sit the heroine on a keg of gun-
powder and expect it to be struck by lightning. You can't
run a business that way.

What these men have got to learn is that the best way of
disposing of a girl with hair the colour of ripe corn is to hit

that hair as hard as possible with a bit of gas-pipe. Buying tarantulas to put in her vanity-bag or little-known Asiatic poisons with which to smear her lipstick do no good whatever and only add to the overhead.

Let them master this fundamental truth, and then we shall see what we shall see.

But even supposing that one day we succeed in ridding mystery fiction of the heroine, can we say sincerely that the Millennium will have arrived? I think not. Even without a feminine interest your average thriller-writer can turn out a pretty painful product.

Of course, there are exceptions. Dorothy Sayers is good. So is Anthony Berkeley. So is Philip Macdonald. So are H. C. Bailey and Agatha Christie. Oppenheim is still the Old Reliable. And nine hundred of every thousand of Edgar Wallace's are worth the seven-and-sixpence every time. But the others . . .

It does not seem to occur to the ordinary man how hard it is to do this sort of thing well, nor does he appear to realize that unless it is done well the result is ghastly. If I had a son who was thinking of writing thrillers—and if I had a son of penholding age that is certainly what he would be doing nowadays—I should take him aside and try to point out some of the drawbacks to this form of authorship.

"James (or John)," I should say, "think well! There is still time to turn aside and write about unhappy marriages and the promiscuous amours of the Intelligentsia. But you have thought it all out, you say? You are resolved to try a mystery story? Then, Edward, the moment has come when you must learn the facts of life. I must tell you that there is a snag in this mystery-story business, and a bad snag. Over every mystery story there broods the shadow of a yawning reader saying 'What of it?'. You inform this reader that Sir Gregory Bulstrode has been murdered in his library. 'Oh, yes?' is his reply, and his manner is indifferent and even bored. He has known so many libraries, you see—such hundreds and hundreds of libraries, and all with corpses in them . . . thin corpses, stout corpses, medium-sized corpses. He has grown to expect corpses in libraries.

"A little discouraged, you add that all the doors and windows were locked.

" 'They always are,' he says.

" 'And suspicion points to at least half a dozen people.'

" 'Oh, well,' he mumbles, dozing off, 'it turns out in the end that one of them did it, I suppose?' "

That is the trouble. For the mystery-novel Suspicion Handicap, the field is so limited. The reader knows it wasn't the hero or heroine who did the murder. He is practically sure it couldn't have been Reggie Banks, because he is a comic character and any vestige of humour in any character in a mystery story automatically rules him out as a potential criminal. It can't have been Uncle Joe, because he is explicitly stated to be kind to dogs. And he naturally rules out all hysterical governesses and brooding butlers, because their behaviour throughout has been so suspicious as to clear them from the start.

So he assumes it must have been some totally uninteresting minor character who hardly ever appears and who is disclosed in the last chapter as the son of the inventor whom the murdered man swindled forty years ago. At any rate, he knows quite well it's one of them.

If I were writing a mystery story, I would go boldly out for the big sensation. I would not have the crime committed by anybody in the book at all. Here are the last few paragraphs of a little thing I have been turning over in my mind against the time when I myself fall a victim to the epidemic.

"You say, Jerningham," I gasped, "that you have solved this inscrutable problem? You really know who it was that put the puncture in Sir Ralph?"

Travers Jerningham nodded curtly. I was astonished to see that he displayed none of the satisfaction which one would naturally have expected. There was a cloud on his forehead and his thin mouth had drawn itself into a tight line.

"I do," he said.

"But you seem gloomy, Jerningham—moody, why is this?"

"Because it is impossible to bring the criminals to justice."

"Criminals? Was there, then, more than one?"

"There were two. Two of the blackest-hearted menaces to Society that ever clutched a knife-handle. One held Sir Ralph down, the other did the stabbing."

"But if you are so sure of this, how is it that you cannot give the scoundrels their just deserts?"

Travers Jerningham laughed a bitter laugh.

"Because, my dear fellow, they aren't in the book at all. The fiends were too cunning to let themselves get beyond the title page. The murderers of Sir Ralph Rackstraw were Messrs. Hodder and Stoughton."

THE END

That would be something like a punch. But the next thing that would happen would be the usual flood of imitations. Somebody would write a thriller in which the crime was traced to Otis and Googe, Bespoke Printers, London, Harringay and Glasgow: and then somebody else would hit on the author's best friend, J. B. Stokes, without whose never-failing sympathy and encouragement this book would not have been written: and so on and so on. You cannot copyright an idea, and times have become so hard for thriller-writers that they are after any possible new murderer like a pack of wolves.

You see, the supply of murderers is giving out. They have all been used so often. You cannot even be sure of the detective's friend now. Ever since Agatha Christie's *Roger Ackroyd* we keep a very sharp eye on that friend. It is very lucky for Doctor Watson that he belonged to the pre-Christie era.

It will be noted that in the above I have stuck to what I might call the Gents' Ordinary or Stock-size detective. Travers Jerningham will be just one more of those curt, hawk-faced amateur investigators. It is not merely that I cannot be bothered to vary the type; I feel that, if you are going to have an amateur investigator, this even now is still the best sort to employ. Try to deviate from the type, and you only find yourself in trouble.

There are three alternatives:

(*a*) The Dry;

(*b*) The Dull;

(*c*) The Effervescent;

and I am not very fond of any of them.

The Dry detective is elderly. He wears pince-nez and a funny hat and is apt to cough primly. He is fussy and old-maidish. Of course, get him in a corner and he suddenly produces a punch like a prize-fighter; but out of his corner he is rather a bore.

Not such a bore, of course, as the Dull detective. This is the one who unmasks the criminals by means of his special knowledge of toxics and things and gets on the villain's track owing to the discovery that the latter is definitely brachiocephalic. Avoid this man.

The Effervescent detective is rather a new invention. He is a bright young fellow of independent means whose hobby is the solution of problems. They like him at Scotland Yard, and he chaffs them. Sometimes Inspector Faraday is a little inclined to shake his head at the young man's suggestions, but he is the first to admit that Tony Dalrymple has an uncanny knack of being right.

And the dear chap is so flippant with it all. None of that "Holmes, who has done this fearful thing?" stuff about him. Violence to the person cannot damp Tony's spirits, provided it is to some other person. Viewing the body brings out all that is gayest and sprightliest in him.

"So this is the jolly old corpse, is it, Inspector? Well, well, well! Bean bashed in and a bit of no-good done to the merry old jugular, what? Tut, tut, mother won't like this at all. You're on to the fact that the merchant who messed this cove up was left-handed and parted his hair in the middle, of course? And a good job he made of it, didn't he?"

Not a frightfully attractive young man. But spreading, I regret to say. You meet him everywhere nowadays.

The best detectives—Edgar Wallace's—are always Scotland Yard men. To a public surfeited with brilliant amateurs there is something very restful about the man from Scotland Yard. He has a background. You can believe in him. If I found it impossible to head my son off from writing mystery stories, I should certainly advise him to give his heroes an official standing. Then he would have the Record and Finger-Print Department at his back, and if he wanted to stop the villain leaving London could tell off three thousand policemen to watch the roads.

It is true that the villain would get through just the same, but you can't say it isn't nice to have the sympathy and moral support of three thousand policemen.

I have got James—or John, as the case may be—pretty clear, then, on the detective end of the job. He has now to face a far more serious problem. What of the villain?

Villains in mystery stories may be divided broadly into three classes—all silly:

(a) Sinister men from China or Assam or Java or India or Tibet (or practically anywhere except Ponder's End and Peebles), who are on the track of the jewel stolen from the temple;

(b) Men with a grudge which has lasted as fresh as ever for thirty years;

(c) Master Criminals.

With regard to (a), I should advise James to try almost anything else first. I rather fancy that sinister jewel-trackers have about reached saturation-point. Besides, what I might call the villain-supplying nationalities have grown so absurdly touchy these days. Make your murderer a Chinaman now, and within a week of your story's appearance letters are pouring into the publisher's office, signed Disgusted Coolie and Mother of Five (Hankow), protesting against the unfair libel. Go elsewhere and you run up against Paterfamilias (Java) and Fair-Play (Tibet). It is not worth it.

And yet the idea of falling back on (b) is not agreeable. The age in which we live is so practical, so matter-of-fact. We are no longer able to believe as readily as our fathers did in the man who cherishes a grudge for a quarter of a century. It was all very well in the old days, when there were fewer distractions, but what with Golf and Tennis and Cross-word Puzzles and the Flat-Race Season and the Jumping Season, and looking after the car and airing the dog and having to learn how to score at Contract Bridge, it seems simply incredible that a man should be able to keep his mind on some unpleasantness which happened in the early spring of 1904.

Which brings us to the last class, Master Criminals.

The psychology of the Master Criminal is a thing I have never been able to understand. I can follow the reasoning of the man who, wishing to put by something for a rainy day, poisons an uncle, shoots a couple of cousins, and forges a will. That is business. It is based on sound commercial principles. But the Master Criminal is simply a ditherer. He does not need money. He has got the stuff. What with the Delancy Emeralds and the Stuyvesant Pearls and the Montresor Holbein and the bearer bonds he stole from the Bank, he must have salted away well over a million. Then what on earth does he want to go on for? Why not retire?

But do you think you could drive that into a Master Criminal's head? Not in a million years. I have just been reading the latest story about one of these poor half-wits. This one, in order to go on being a Master Criminal, was obliged to live in a broken-down cellar on a smelly wharf on the river, posing as a lodging-house keeper. All he did with his time was chop wood in the backyard. And at a conservative estimate, after paying salaries to his staff of one-eyed Chinamen, pock-marked Mexicans, and knife-throwing deaf-mutes, he must have been worth between two and three million pounds.

He could have had a yacht, a fleet of motor-cars, a house in Grosvenor Square, a nice place in the country, a bit of shooting in Scotland, a few miles of fishing on some good river, a villa on the Riviera, and a racing-stable. He could have run a paper, revived British opera, and put on Shakespeare at popular prices. But no, he preferred to go on living in his riverside cellar, which was flooded every time there was a high tide, simply because he wanted to be a Master Criminal.

One scarcely knows whether to laugh or weep.

I remember one Master Criminal, just as rich as this man, who set his whole organization at work for weeks digging a tunnel into a bank. And what do you think he got out of it? Twelve thousand pounds. Not guineas. Pounds.

Twelve thousand pounds! Can you beat it? Just about what I am paid for writing this article.

Perhaps, on the whole, then, James, you had better avoid all three of the types of villain which I have mentioned and stick to the Fiend in Human Shape. This variety has the enormous advantage that he has not got to be made plausible. He is a homicidal lunatic, and as such can get away with anything. To the man with the thirty-year-old grudge we say, "But, my dear fellow, consider. If you stick that knife into Sir George, what of the future? What will you do in the long winter evenings with no dream of vengeance to nurse?" To the Master Criminal we point out that he is giving himself a lot of trouble to add to an income which is already absurdly large. He cannot *like* having to put on false whiskers and stand outside the hero's bedroom on a chilly night, pumping poison-gas through it, or enjoy climbing up a slippery roof to drop cobras down the chimney. But the Fiend in Human Shape we merely pat encouragingly on the back and speed on his way with a cheery "Good luck, Fiend, old man! Go as far as you like!"

And he gnashes his teeth amiably and snaps into it with an animal snarl.

Round and About the Theatre

1. Fair Play for Audiences

IN an age full, like the present, of Moot Questions—some mooter than others, others possibly a shade less moot than some—perhaps the mootest question of any is: Why has nobody ever taken steps to secure Justice and Fair Play for Theatre Audiences? We have societies for the prevention of cruelty to children, to animals, to everything else you can think of, but none for the prevention of cruelty to the people who pay money to see plays.

And it is no use, Mr. Everyman, trying to dodge the question by saying that people who are foolish enough to pay money to see the sort of plays that are put on nowadays deserve to suffer. That is not the point. Theatre audiences may not be the brightest people in the world, but they are people. They are human. They are—practically—God's creatures. And something has got to be done about them.

I have been reading an article by an actress which puts the case for this downtrodden class excellently.

"To an unjaundiced eye," she says, "an audience is a nightly miracle. Amiability is a matter of health, and think what an unhealthy life an audience leads. Always indoors, always with indigestion after a hurried meal, and always suffering from cold feet. Cooped up in a chair, and forbidden to argue or snore or groan or cry for help. And all it has to look forward to, besides the end of the play, is walking home. Yet there it sits, night after night, watching politely, even

47

bending forward sometimes with a look of eager interest. And never answering back."

There you have the thing in a nutshell. It leaves out all the minor tribulations of these poor peons, such as the hurrying from the dinner-table to the theatre at the advertised time for the rise of the curtain and the long, restful wait of twenty-five minutes till the curtain actually rises. It does not touch on the odd fact that theatre-architects seem to imagine that the human race is a race of midgets without legs, and construct their seats accordingly. But it does speak a much-needed word for a persecuted and suffering class of the community, and one hopes that in future critics who are contemplating attacks on the audience will restrain themselves.

Attacks? Oh yes, there have been attacks. Only the other day the vaudeville critic of an American theatrical paper was saying all sorts of nasty things.

Usually, where the critics are concerned, the audience gets off pretty lightly. Critics as a class confine themselves to rending the play and the performers. Occasionally one of them, after savaging a piece and jumping on it with both feet and generally proclaiming its unfitness to be considered part of the scheme of things, will add a scornfully pitying line to the effect that "The audience, however, seemed to be pleased". He may feel tempted to add "poor fools", but he resists the temptation.

This particular vaudeville critic, however, was made of sterner stuff.

"Business", he begins, "on Wednesday evening was big, and an audience which was mentally unequal to the quality of vaudeville which it had paid to see was as satisfied as that kind of an audience knows how to be."

He then proceeds to details.

"Beulah Bellamy was never better in her life. Her songs went right over the heads of the flat-heads out in front, but even a deaf-and-dumb bricklayer with one good eye couldn't help liking her."

And, later in the outburst, in connexion with a cross-talk turn:

"The dialogue was witty, but just because these men did not hand it out to the boneheads in front with a thick syrup of low comedy, the sad-eyed kitchen-mechanics failed to rise to the bait."

After that, he does not say a single derogatory thing about the audience. He seems to consider that he has spoken his mind.

It is to be hoped that other critics will not follow his lead and make this method of writing the fashion. Apart from the inhumanity of it, it is so easily capable of development, and the step from attacking audiences in the mass to singling out individuals for censure is so short.

I should hate to read in my morning paper, after visiting a theatre, that "James Gagger's new number is a winner and took three encores failing, however, to get a murmur out of a bald-headed, spectacled plug-ugly who sat on our left and badly needed a shave and brush-up. We were sufficiently interested to make inquiries and ascertained the identity of this goggle-eyed misfit. The name is Wodehouse, initials P. G., and, as he is well known to the police, any constable will direct you to his residence, should you wish to burn it down. If you meet him in the street, kick him. He ought not to be at large."

Going to the theatre would become in these circumstances even more of a risk than it is at present.

For it is a risk, and of the deadliest kind. And that is why it is wrong to say unkind things about audiences. The man who goes to see a play may be half-witted, but he is a sports-man and should be entitled to consideration as such.

What it amounts to is that he has betted—blindly—good money that he will not be bored. If he loses his bet, as he generally does, it is very decent of him merely to sit still and say nothing. If he were not a very fine fellow, he would make a demonstration of some kind. He would ring up the manager late at night and tell him the show was awful and that his money had been obtained under false pretences. Or he would tear up the seats or something. But being a sports-man, he just pockets his loss in silence.

When you consider what audiences are called upon to go through, their sunny patience is marvellous. They are tricked and bullied into the theatre. Day after day they are shouted at in the advertisement columns of the Press and assured that they are taking no risk in putting down their money. It is implied that if they hold back they ought to be ashamed of themselves and will spend a lifetime of regret when it is too late. And finally they give in, only to discover that they have been fooled again.

Yes, these things are going on in our very midst unchecked, without protest. It is the sort of evil John Galsworthy ought to write a scorcher about, and the extraordinary thing is that he has not yet done so.

What is at the root of the audience's unfortunate position is the old business of Taxation Without Representation. That is to say, the management of the theatre takes the audience's money but won't allow it a voice in the subse-quent proceedings..

This is particularly noticeable in musical comedy. In every musical comedy nowadays there is a Big Number. It is big purely because the management has decided that it is big. "We'll scrape along somehow to the middle of Act Two,"

says the management—I have not tried to convey the actual
sound of the management's words, because I am not good
at dialect, but the "We'll" should of course be "Ve'll" . . .
Very well then, where was I? Ah yes.

"Ve'll thscrape along somehow to the middle of Act Two,"
says the management, "and then ve'll knock 'em cold vit our
big number, 'Vill you vait for me in the moonlight?' "

The thing is a deliberate plot. The dance-director is in-
structed to think up a lot of different business for first encore,
second encore, third encore, and so on. The chorus is drilled
to the last smile. Old Bill in the flies is told just when to
switch on ambers and blues. And then the number comes on.

Well, the audience listens, sniffs at it, turns it over with
its paws, and then leans back so as to intimate that that in
its opinion is that, and now let's get on with the story and
see what happens when the hero meets the adventuress again.

But does the management let it go at that and permit
bygones to be bygones? Not by any means. This is the big
number, and it's going to be the big number, even if everybody out in front dies where he sits. What does the audience
think they brought the dance-director over from America for
and are paying him a vast salary for? Fun? Amusement?
The mere pleasure of seeing him about the place? In the
midst of the pained hush that pervades the auditorium like a
fog the conductor taps with his baton, the orchestra strikes
up the refrain, and out come the chorus for encore number
one.

At the conclusion of this there is a little sporadic applause.
The audience, having the souls of gentlemen, are willing to
show the performers that they bear no ill will and that, now
that the awful thing is really over, they are prepared to bury
the past and, so to speak, start a new life together.

At this moment, the conductor taps with his baton again,

that beastly glutinous refrain begins once more, and out come the chorus again. From this point on, the audience is licked. It just sits there and hopes for the end. It knows that nothing it can do, short of the only sensible thing—viz. pulling the theatre down and murdering the management—can stop that song until the last encore has been repeated twice; so it makes the best of it, chats in a low voice about the weather, reads What The Smart Man Will Wear page in the programme, and thinks of its boyhood. And presently, when the management's passion for encores is glutted, the play goes on.

This is not an isolated arbitrary act. The theatre is run all the time on the principle that the audience has no say in anything. Suppose a small-part actor pleases the customers and they want to see more of him? What can they do? The management ignores their preferences and plugs along with the star. Revolutions have come about for smaller reasons, and against tyranny slighter than this whole populations have arisen in rebellion.

Which brings me to my real point, which is that audiences have been tolerant too long and the time has come to take a strong line. Actors have a Union now. So have playwrights. So have stage-hands. And so have electricians. Annoy Old Bill up in the flies, and he will leave his blues and ambers flat and walk out till his conditions are bettered. Why, then, should not playgoers follow the example of all the other sections of the theatrical community which are rallying together for mutual protection, and announce formally that, if managers, actors and dramatists do not mend their ways, they will take steps?

In the past, as I have pointed out, audiences' lamentable lack of organization has resulted in serious abuses. But even audiences can be pushed too far, and the moment has arrived for them to assert themselves. As they are numerous, so let them be resolute. Let them show that they mean business. Let them say to their persecutors, "If you managers, actors and dramatists accede to our reasonable demands, we will continue to buy tickets for your performances on such occasions as it shall prove impossible for us to get free seats. If, under-estimating our power, you are so reckless as to defy us, we shall simply abstain from theatre-going till you come to your senses. When eight o'clock arrives, instead of bolting the last mouthful and rushing out, we shall stay at home, put on the old slippers, light the good old pipe, and tune in on the B.B.C.'s lecture on the private life of the newt. You need have no hope that you can bring us to heel. Believe us or believe us not, if we really put our minds to it, we can stay away from the theatre indefinitely."

The downtreading of the playgoer has been going on so long that the demands of the Amalgamated Brotherhood of Ticket Buyers will of necessity be extremely numerous. If the reforms demanded seem at first sight excessive, it must be remembered that the onus of blame lies with the managers, actors and dramatists. It is their fault that there is any need for these reforms.

I will now proceed to sketch out a few of the demands which the new Brotherhood will make.

First, as concerns the Managers.

It has been the playful custom of managers in the past to announce an entertainment to begin at eight-twenty and, having caused the playgoer to raise his blood-pressure to dangerous heights in the effort to get to the theatre in time, to start the performance at a quarter to nine. This must stop. The Brotherhood will allow two minutes' grace. At eight-twenty-two the audience will file out of the building, tearing up the seats as it goes, and, after raiding the box-office and recovering its money, will depart, never to return. There will be no exception to this rule.

Secondly, if any Brother pays twelve shillings for a stall and finds himself placed behind a pillar at the junction-point of two (2) draughts, the Brotherhood will strike. If the management tries to economize by doing without an orchestra, on the flimsy pretext that the audience's musical ear will be equally entertained by hearing a stage-hand bang three times on the floor with a chunk of wood, the Brotherhood will strike. If any interval is longer than any act, the Brotherhood will strike.

Now, as regards the Dramatists.

The Amalgamated Brotherhood of Ticket Buyers will hold to strict accountability any dramatist who writes a play in which the poor workman marries the daughter of his employer, in which a bank cashier has an extravagant wife, in which there is a court scene, in which a dead body falls out of

(a) The fireplace,
(b) The bookcase,
(c) The chest of drawers,

or in which more than one (1) American detective in a bowler hat appears.

Farce-writers will be required to disavow farces in which use is made of more than two (2) doors, in which the motive for the leading performer's actions is a desire to deceive his wife, or in which any character or characters hides or hide behind a screen or screens.

Diplomatic negotiations will be broken off with all manufacturers of sentimental plays in which elderly guardians marry—or fail to marry through voluntary self-sacrifice—their wards; in which any scene is accomplished by music off-stage; or in which any character or characters looks or look at a locket or lockets containing the photograph or photographs of his or their mother or mothers.

As to musical pieces, the plugging of any number beyond the point which medical science has established as dangerous to human life will be regarded as a deliberately unfriendly act.

Thirdly, and lastly, let us address the Actors.

The Amalgamated Brotherhood of Ticket Buyers will omit no word or act to restrain performers:

(1) If male:

from

(a) Proposing to the heroine down the back of her neck,

(b) Lighting more than six (6) cigarettes in the course of an evening,

(c) Using the telephone more than five (5) times in an act, and

(2) If female:

from

(a) Laughing mockingly, hysterically or defiantly,

(b) Sniffing emotionally and letting her shoulders heave,

(c) Expressing her inability to stand something which is torturing her,

(d) Uttering epigrams about Life.

Those will be the Brotherhood's preliminary demands. Others will, no doubt, be added from time to time. Suffering will undoubtedly be caused and many dramatists will have to give up their trade and go back to work; but we must not allow this to deter us. Think what would have happened to Magna Charta if the Barons had gone about saying "This is rather rough on poor old John." You cannot, if I may coin a phrase, make an omelette without breaking eggs. We must be firm. For years playgoers have been ground beneath the iron heel. Let them now get together and do a bit of grinding themselves.

2.   *Looking Back at the Halls*

I SUPPOSE the music-hall as an institution must now be written down as definitely a thing of the past. The Oxford is no more. The Empire and the Tivoli are motion-picture houses. The London Pavilion wavers between films and revues. And the Alhambra has gone in for musical spectacles on the grand scale.

I am sorry for this, as I have always had just the sort of mentality which the music-hall satisfied. It took strong men to drag me to see Tree in *Julius Cæsar*, but if Harry Tate's Motoring was on in Islington I was there in two jumps. Sentimentalizing about the halls is the one sure sign of senile decay, and I do it all the time. Surprise me nodding over my coffee at the club, and you will be very lucky if you escape without a word or two about Dan Leno or Lottie Collins. Those, if I may say so, were the days.

As a matter of fact, I don't think I ever saw Lottie Collins. But many is the morning when you could have heard me rendering her best-known number in a shrill treble in my bath. I suppose it is forgotten now, but here is how the refrain went. You start at the top and read straight down.

> *Ta-ra-ra-boom-de-ay!*
> *Ta-ra-ra-boom-de-ay!*
> *Ta-ra-ra-boom-de-ay!*
> *Ta-ra-ra-boom-de-ay!*
> *Ta-ra-ra-boom-de-ay!*
> *Ta-ra-ra-boom-de-ay!*
> *Ta-ra-ra-boom-de-ay!*
> *Ta-ra-ra-boom-de-ay!*

The author always considered that a pretty good lyric, and

its popularity showed that the public endorsed his view. He was one of those slow, careful workers who chisel and polish every line of a song before letting it out of their hands. He wrote the last line first and worked up to it. He always used a blunt pen, and could not write unless there were roses in the flower-bowl on his desk. His favourite poet was Shelley, to whom, he frankly admitted, he owed much.

It was at about this period that the Patriotic Song really flourished. In those days, when you went to a music-hall, you were certain to be confronted, at about ten o'clock, by a stout man in baggy evening-dress with a diamond solitaire in his shirt-front, who walked on the stage in a resolute way and stood glaring at you with one hand in the arm-hole of his waistcoat.

You knew he wasn't a juggler or a conjurer, because he had no props and no female assistant in pink tights. And you knew he wasn't a dramatic twenty-minute sketch, because he would have had a gang along with him. And presently your worst fears were confirmed, when he began to sing a patriotic song with some such refrain as:

> For England's England still
> It is and always will.
> Though foreign foes may brag,
> We love our dear old flag,
> And old England is En-ger-land still.

Then he was got off somehow and a comedian came on.

It has always seemed to me a remarkable proof that even as a boy my judgment was sound and good that, while I have never experienced the slightest desire to go on the legitimate stage, it was my earliest ambition to become a comedian on the halls.

Even at the tender age of twelve, the music-hall appealed to the artist in me, and, though still a child, I could perceive that to succeed in it one must possess many of the nobler qualities. I gave up my boyhood dreams reluctantly, but my admiration for the men who had got there remained, and I have never been able to dismiss the music-hall comedian with a contemptuous gesture, as many people do, on the ground that he was a member of an ignoble profession and not fit to be classed among the world's uplifters.

To succeed on the halls, you had to have special gifts. You could not get by through influence or mere amiability of disposition. You could not go into vaudeville, as you can go on the legitimate stage, to amuse yourself or to tide over a lean period when your allowance has been cut off. In no other walk of life was the individual so straitly tested. It was because a music-hall comedian required vim, pep, *espièglerie*, a good singing voice, and a sort of indefinable *je-ne-sais-quoi*— none of which qualities I appeared to possess—that I abandoned my ambitions and became a writer.

It was the loneliness of the job that made it so hard. The music-hall artist was right out in the open, with no support. You remember how you used to feel when they dragged you down to the drawing-room and made you recite "The Wreck of the Hesperus". Well, that was how music-hall artists must have felt all the time. The heroine of a musical comedy has the support and approval of a chorus of seventy-five. They follow her about. They bound in the background during her songs. They make her feel that they, at least, are strong for her.

It was different for the music-hall performer. He started his turn on an empty stage, all alone in a hard world. If there was to be any support and approval, it must come from the audience—that sullen, glowering, set-jawed throng: and he had got to do something immediately to galvanize them into life with a jerk. And yet people who feel sorry for David when he sang before Saul and found himself in such a tough spot will tell you that music-hall artists earned their money easily.

Nor was loneliness the only drawback to the lives of these intrepid men. The fierceness of the competition was another, though it did not affect singers so much as other performers. There was something miraculous in the ability of the denizens of the vaudeville world to reproduce any successful turn with practically no delay whatever.

Let us suppose that, after much tense thought and studious practice, you had perfected some unusual act. Let us say that you burst on an astonished public as Dare-Devil Desmond, the only man in the world who could ride a motor-bicycle head-downwards across the ceiling. Do not imagine for an instant that you would have been allowed to enjoy the fruits of your enterprise unchallenged. In about two weeks, a horde of rivals, doing the same turn just as well, would appear on every circuit, and by the end of the season your speciality would have become stale, and in order to get bookings you would have to invent something else with a little more punch in it.

Furthermore, there were no limits to the amount the public demanded for its money. On the legitimate stage, if an actor wears a decent suit of clothes and speaks his lines satisfactorily, his audience is satisfied. He is not expected to fill out with a bit of trick juggling or a ballroom dance. But on the halls it was quite another matter. Take, for example, the case of the music-hall juggler. To the ordinary man who cannot carry a teacup across a room without spilling its contents and nearly dropping it twice, it would seem, no doubt, that anyone who could balance a chair, two vases, three billiard-balls, a cue, and a female assistant on the tip of his nose was doing enough to earn his salary, and should not have been called upon to elaborate his performance.

But on the halls a trifling feat like this was but a beginning. A juggler was looked askance at if he loafed. While doing this balancing-act, the least his audience would permit him to supplement it with was a little rapid work with some plates in his left hand, while with his right he would be expected to throw up and catch in brisk succession a few dozen rubber balls. And even then people were inclined to ask themselves if the fellow couldn't find something to do with his feet.

In addition to this, the poor man had to be a finished comedian and keep up a rapid fire of humorous observations on this and that. There used to be an excellent violinist who could only secure bookings by playing with the instrument behind his back. And, at that, he had to sing a couple of comic songs as well. And unthinking people grudged these men their money.

I often used to wonder how music-hall performers first got the idea of becoming music-hall performers. My own case, of course, was rather different. I just wanted to sing. And everybody wants to sing. But how did the man who dived through a hole in the roof into a small tank first get the impulse?

One pictures him studying peacefully for the Church, without a thought of any other walk in life, when suddenly, one evening as he sits among his theological books, a thought flashes upon him. "This is all very well," whispers some inward voice, "but what you were really intended to do was to dive through roofs into tanks. Do not stifle your individuality. Remember the parable of the talents." So he throws away his books and goes off to see somebody in Maiden Lane about a try-out at Wigan.

But where and how did he practise? There was a man at the old Madison Square Garden in New York years ago who used to stand on one of the girders which supported the roof and dive head-foremost on to a sloping chute. Down this he would slide on his stomach, finally turning a somersault in mid-air and alighting on his feet with a simper of modest pride, as who should say, "You thought I was a chump when I started that dive—didn't you, now?" The mind pauses baffled at the contemplation of the steps that led up to that perfected feat. The early rehearsals must have been worth seeing.

3. *An Outline of Shakespeare*

THE fact that the anniversary of Shakespeare's birth occurs this year leads me to feel that a brief paper on this great writer—or as some say, this famous literary syndicate—will not be amiss. And when I say Shakespeare, do not run away with the idea that I am not perfectly aware that it may have been Shakespere or even Shikspur. I have the situation well in hand.

As I have hinted above, there are two sharply divided schools of thought regarding Shakespeare. The larger of these two schools reverences him as the author of the plays that bear his name and sums the thing up rather neatly by saying that others may abide our question but that he is free. And it will, I think, be admitted that nothing could be fairer than that.

But, just as there will always be at every conjuring entertainment a small part of the Left muttering to one another, "It's up his sleeve!" so in this matter of Shakespeare's plays is there a carping minority who hold that he did not write them at all but simply lent his name to a limited company consisting of Sir Francis Bacon, Sir Walter Raleigh, the Earl of Oxford, the Earl of Essex, Queen Elizabeth, Mr. Gordon Selfridge, and the second girl from the end in the front row of the chorus of the Merry Widow No. 1 Touring Company.

All the work that Shakespeare did, they maintain, was to practise spelling his signature on the covers of the typed scripts. At the most, they say, he was merely what is now known as a "dramatic fixer": and in support of this contention a Baconian of my acquaintance tells a story which he claims to be thoroughly documented—only, unfortunately, in a cipher which nobody but he can read.

It seems, according to this man, that Bacon, best known to the reading public of his day as the author of two bright little works entitled *The Novum Organum* and *De Interpretatione Naturæ*, had always had the firm conviction that he could write a corking play. He was, in short, a dreamer. Aren't we all? So in the intervals of looking after the Exchequer (of which, it will be remembered, he was the genial and popular Chancellor) he sat down with the old quill and ink-horn and dashed off a tragedy called *Hamlet*.

He then began sending it round to the managers.

The first manager kept it six months, and when Bacon wrote inquiring after it sent him back a farcical comedy by some other gentleman, regretting that it was not in his power, much as he admired it personally, to produce the same.

Bacon sighed and sent another copy to another manager.

When a year had elapsed, he wrote, apologizing for what might seem impatience on his part, but asking if any decision on his drama *Hamlet* had been arrived at. A few days later, he received by the same post his manuscript and a letter from the manager's secretary saying that there was evidently some mistake, for no such manuscript had been received at the office.

By this time Bacon had begun to realize, as so many have realized since, that things theatrical are inseparable from a sort of brisk delirium associated only with the interiors of homes for the feeble-minded. And he had just resolved to give the thing up and start on another book of essays when quite unexpectedly a manager who had had the script three years and had quite gone out of his mind (Bacon's mind) wrote asking him to call. And after waiting four hours in the outer office with a crowd of blue-chinned men who were telling one another how they had jumped in and saved the show when they were with the Earl of Worcester's Company, he was shown in.

"Now, this what's-its-name of yours," said the manager, "this *Hamlet*—of course, we'll have to alter the title—I think it's got a chance. There's some good stuff in it. But it needs fixing."

"Fixing?"

"Couldn't put it on as it stands. The public wouldn't look at it. You're new at this game, I suppose?"

Bacon muttered something about having done a bit of writing.

"Not plays?"

"Essays."

"Essays!" said the manager, with a short laugh. "Well, as I was saying, we'll have to get this thing fixed. And the man to do it is young Shakespeare. Clever boy. In my company. He'll soon put it right. Now about terms. You get one per cent. of the gross."

Bacon, who as Chancellor of the Exchequer was pretty good at figures, protested that one per cent. of the gross was not much.

"Sweetheart," said the manager, "don't you begin opening your mouth too wide, like the rest of them. When you came into this office, I said to myself, 'There's a sensible, level-headed young chap,' I said to myself. 'You won't find him wanting the earth.' You aren't going to make me alter my opinion? Of course you aren't. Why, you might make a pile out of one per cent. Sign here."

A shrewd man, Bacon realized that there was nothing else for him to do. The superstition current in theatrical circles that there was a kind of magic in play-writing, and that nobody could fathom the mysteries of the craft unless he was one of the small coterie who spent their time in the Mermaid Tavern buying sack for managers, was too strong for him. He knew his *Hamlet* was good, but he had gathered by this time that he would never get it produced unless he consented to hand it over to the men who had been "twenty years in the business" to pull to pieces. So he signed the contract, and the manager sent round to the Mermaid for Shakespeare.

Two days later they all lunched together at that hostelry. Shakespeare had the script with him, and directly the meal was over he produced a fat sheaf of notes.

"Well, laddie," said Shakespeare, "I've read your little thing, and I think I can do something with it. But it wants a lot of working on. For one thing, your finish is weak. What you want at the final curtain is to have the whole crowd jump on one another and everybody kill everybody else. We'll have the King poison the wine and Laertes poison the sword and then Laertes plugs Hamlet with the sword and drops it and Hamlet picks it up in mistake for his own and plugs Laertes, and then the Queen drinks the wine and Hamlet sticks the King with poisoned sword. Then you'll have got something."

"Swell!" said the manager.

"But surely," argued Bacon, "isn't all that a little improbable?"

"It's what the public wants," said Shakespeare coldly. "Or maybe you think I don't know?"

"Sure he knows you know, Bill," interposed the manager soothingly. "Don't get your shirt out. We're all working for the good of the show. Anything else?"

"Is there anything else!" cried Shakespeare. "Why, there's nothing else but something else. For one thing, he's made his hero a loony."

"His sufferings drove him mad," said Bacon.

"Not in any play I'm going to have anything to do with his sufferings didn't," retorted Shakespeare. "Listen! I've been in this business . . ."

"'S all right, Bill, 's all right," said the manager, patting his arm. "Mr. Bacon's not arguing. You see, Mr. Bacon," he went on soothingly, "we've got to think of the matinée girl. The matinée girl doesn't like loonies. You've got to consider every angle in this game. So you'll make him not crazy, Bill?"

"I'll do better than that," said Shakespeare. "I'll make him *pretend* to be crazy. See? Everybody's fooled but the audience."

"I told you this boy was clever," murmured the manager to Bacon, who had turned rather pale and was beginning to mutter a little to himself.

"Gives a chance for comedy," said Shakespeare.

"So it does," said the manager. "But I'll tell you what I'm sure Bill here will do to meet you. He'll make the girl, Ophelia, loony. That'll be all right. An audience doesn't mind a crazy girl."

"All girls are crazy, anyway," said Shakespeare, speaking in rather a peevish tone, as if he had been reminded of some private grievance. "But, coming back to this comedy angle, I'll write in a scene where Hamlet kids the two 'Varsity boys."

"That'll be fine," said the manager. "It'll go well on Boat Race night."

Shakespeare was frowning thoughtfully as he turned his notes.

" 'To be or not to be . . .' " he murmured. "I'm wondering about that 'To be or not to be' speech. The public don't like soliloquies."

Bacon was now thoroughly roused.

"Yeah?" he said.

"Yeah," said Shakespeare.

"Says you!" said Bacon.

"Yes, says me!" retorted Shakespeare.

"How about Eugene O'Neill?" said Bacon.

"That's all right about Eugene O'Neill," said Shakespeare. "Those Yanks'll do anything."

"Now, now, boys," pleaded the manager pacifically. "Don't let's get worked up about this. I was looking at that speech myself, Bill. It gives the stage-hands time to set the scene behind the front cloth. I'd keep it in, I think."

"All right," said Shakespeare. "But if it's to stay in it's got to be longer. I'll write in a line or two. How's this for one? 'Or to take arms against a sea of troubles'? I thought of that this minute. Just like a flash."

"You can't take arms against a sea," said Bacon. "It's a mixed metaphor."

"Who says it's a mixed metaphor?"

"I say it's a mixed metaphor."

"Boys!" said the manager.

"Oh, put it in, put it in," said Bacon, rising.

"You going, Mr. Bacon?" said the manager.

"Yes," said Bacon. "To take a couple of aspirins and try to forget."

He did not attend the opening of *Hamlet* or any subsequent performance.

That is the story my Baconian acquaintance tells. And when I asked him how it came about that no mention of Bacon's share in the authorship of this great drama has come down to us, he had his answer for that.

Shakespeare, he says, did offer to have the bills read as follows:

HAMLET

by

WILLIAM SHAKESPEARE

and

FRANCIS BACON

but Bacon, after attending the first rehearsal and reading the revised script, absolutely refused to have his name connected with the production in any way.

That, as I say, is the attitude of a good many people towards Shakespeare and his claims to be ranked as the world's greatest author, but I, personally, do not take much stock in it. I prefer to believe the more generally accepted story, of which this is a brief outline.

Born in the year 1564, and baptized on April the twenty-sixth, it was not immediately that the Bard of Avon turned his attention to the drama. In his early youth he seems to have had the idea that there was a good living to be made out of stealing rabbits from the preserves of the local squires, and it was only when approaching years of discretion that it suddenly occurred to him that a man could do much better for himself by stealing plots. In the year 1591 he began to write plays, and from then onward anybody who had a good plot put it in a steel-bound box and sat on the lid when he saw Shakespeare coming.

There was, of course, some excuse for the young fellow. He was the official playwright to a company of actors, and they worked him so hard that there was simply no time for him to think out his own plots. In those days a good run for a play was two nights. Anything over this was sensational.

Shakespeare, therefore, would dash off *Macbeth* on Sunday night for production on Monday, and on Tuesday morning at six o'clock round would come Burbage in a great state of excitement.

"Good heavens, William, why aren't you up and working? Don't you know we've got to give 'em something to-night?"

"What about *Macbeth*?" Shakespeare would ask sleepily.

"*Macbeth* finished its long and successful run last night, and if you haven't got something to follow we'll have to close the theatre."

So Shakespeare would heave himself out of bed, dig down into the box where he kept other people's plots, and by lunch-time he would hand Burbage the script of *Othello*. And Burbage would skim through it and say it was rotten but it would have to do.

A playwright cannot give of his best under these conditions, and this, to my mind, accounts for a peculiarity in Shakespeare's work which has, I believe, escaped the notice of critics—to wit, the fact that, while his stuff sounds all right, it generally doesn't mean anything. It cannot be doubted that, when he was pushed for time, William Shakespeare just shoved down anything and trusted to the charity of the audience to pull him through. Burbage was popping in and out every two minutes, asking him when the deuce he was going to get that script finished, so down went the first thing that came into his head.

"What on earth does 'abroach' mean?" Burbage would ask, puzzled, halting the rehearsal of *Romeo and Juliet*.

"It's something girls wear," Shakespeare would say. "You know. Made of diamonds and fastened with a pin."

"But you say, 'Who set this ancient quarrel new abroach?' and it doesn't seem to me to make sense."

"Oh, it's all in the acting," Shakespeare would say. "You just speak the line quick and nobody'll notice anything."

And that would be that, till they were rehearsing *Pericles, Prince of Tyre*, and somebody had to say to somebody else, "I'll fetch thee with a wanion". Shakespeare would get round that by pretending that a wanion was a sort of cab, but this gave him only a brief respite, because the next moment they would be asking him what a "geck" was, or a "loggat", or a "cullion", or an "egma", or a "punto" or a "span-counter", and wanting to know what he meant by saying a character had become "frampold" because he was so "rawly". It was a wearing life, and though Shakespeare would try to pass it off jocularly by telling the boys at the Mermaid that it was all in a lifetime and the first hundred years were the hardest and all that sort of thing, there can be little doubt that he felt the strain.

So if he wanted to steal plots, good luck to him, say I for one.

There seems to be no question that Shakespeare had all the usual struggles of the beginner who tries to break into the play-writing game. Tradition says that he started in a modest way by holding horses at the theatre doors, and a moving historical picture might be painted of the future king of the English stage, trying to read Burbage the opening scene of a comedy while the latter flitted past on his way to the Mermaid, and at the same time endeavouring to elude the attentions of a peevish destrier or charger who was trying to bite him in the back of the neck.

Eventually, however, merit found its way to the top, and our hero became a member of a London company. It was shortly after this that he began to get his plays accepted.

Things were not made easy for him at any period of his career. Just as he had succeeded in getting a footing and was beginning to tot up how much his royalties would amount to if they played to fifteen ducats, four pieces of eight, and a rose noble on the Saturday night, the Plague broke out, and from the beginning of February 1593 the theatres were closed. He wrote *Titus Andronicus*, and got it produced in 1594, and then back came the Plague and closed the theatres again.

But you cannot keep a good man down, and by this time Shakespeare had started to steal his plots, so that he could now produce dramas almost without conscious effort. The result was that when the theatre opened again he was ready for it. He had *The Taming of the Shrew, Love's Labour's Lost,* and *Romeo and Juliet* put on before the year was over. After that, they saw that it was no good closing the theatres.

Of his first piece little is known, but the fact that it is said to have been written in collaboration with Marlowe, Greene, and Peele makes it seem probable that it was a musical comedy. No doubt Shakespeare wrote the original book, Marlowe added extra scenes, Greene contributed additional lines, and Peele inserted supplementary material. It does not appear to have been a great success, thus emphasizing the hopelessness of trying to do a piece of this kind without Leslie Henson and Heather Thatcher.

A good deal of mystery surrounds both the private life and the artistic career of William Shakespeare. Nobody seems to know what he did with his time, where he lived, whom he married, and what he looked like. He is generally supposed to have married Anne Hathaway, but there is an entry in an existing register relating to the wedding of "William Shakespeare" and "Annam Whately de Temple Grafton". One can only suppose that the clerk was a weaker speller than the bridegroom himself and that this was his plucky, though scarcely successful, attempt at writing "Anne Hathaway". At that, it would not have been at all a bad shot for those times.

As regards his appearance, there are sixteen portraits of him in the book of reference to which I owe so grateful a debt, and except that they are all solid on the fact that he never shaved, each is absolutely different from the others. Of course, it must have been difficult to paint Shakespeare's portrait. He was always either rushing on to the stage to play a part, or else seated at Burbage's desk in the room marked "No admittance" toiling away at a new drama: and you had to get the best view of him you could through the keyhole.

It is, of course, possible that, absorbed as he was by his work, he had to have himself painted by the correspondence method. He may have been compelled to confine himself to describing by letter what he thought he looked like and leaving the rest to the ingenuity of the artist.

Sports and Pastimes

1. The Decay of Falconry

THERE was a paragraph in the papers the other day to the effect that an Eton boy was advertising a reward for his lost falcon: and it came as something of a surprise to me to learn that in this present year of grace somebody possessed one of these birds. Is there an Eton and Harrow match for falcons? Do Bishops and Generals smash each other's hats at Lord's when the long, nerve-racking game is over and the old school has won by two herons? Apparently, yes. But this must be the very last stand of that once popular sport.

For it would be idle to deny that of recent years Hawking as a pastime has lost its hold on the British public almost completely. A man going about the countryside to-day with a bird attached to his wrist would excite remark: and if he were overheard addressing it as his "tassel gentle", serious trouble might ensue with the Lunacy Commissioners. The motto of the present century is: Golf and the world golfs with you; hawk and you hawk alone.

According to the *Encyclopædia Britannica*, to which I occasionally turn to polish up my information on the few things I do not already know all about, this state of affairs was brought about by the enclosure of waste lands, agricultural improvements, and the introduction of fire-arms into the sporting field.

With all deference to the writer, I cannot see what the second of these items had to do with it. A hawker does not hawk less eagerly because he has just bought an up-to-date brand of guano or a self-propelling plough. Nor would a really enthusiastic falconer be stopped by the mere fact that waste lands had been enclosed. He would simply hop over the fence. What really dealt the pastime its death-blow was that introduction of fire-arms into the sporting field. Once guns came in, it was simply a question of time before falcons were handed their hats.

Right from the beginning there had been a flaw in Falconry, a drawback to the sport, and thinking men saw it in a flash. It was this—that the hawk got all the fun and applause, while the human being who was paying its board and lodging was merely a super, supporting the star. Faced with the alternative of watching a bird amuse itself and of having the time of their lives peppering game-keepers with small shot, British sportsmen did not hesitate. Tired of playing second fiddle to a mere bird, they grabbed eagerly for their guns: and from that moment Falconry was doomed.

Another reason why the sport waned in favour was that it was essentially undemocratic. It failed to cater for the man of small means who is the backbone of every national game. "Falcons and hawks", says one writer, "were allotted to degrees and orders of men according to rank and station—for instance, to the Emperor the eagle or vulture, to royalty the jer-falcon, to an earl the peregrine, to a yeoman the goshawk, to a priest the sparrow-hawk, and to a knave or servant the useless kestrel."

Anybody could have told them that that sort of thing would not do in a progressive age. One can readily imagine the chagrin of the knave or servant when compelled to listen to the earl boasting of how Percy, his peregrine, had gone round that morning in two over bogey, conscious the while that the handicap of Kenneth, his own kestrel, still stuck steadily in the late twenties, its game, in spite of tuition from the local pro., showing absolutely no signs of improvement.

You could not have Falconry nowadays on anything like its former scale. For one thing, modern civilization has grown too complex. True, the curate could still be allotted his sparrow-hawk (which would probably bite him and tend to embitter the tone of his sermons), but how could the committee who looked after these matters possibly satisfy everybody in these times? There would not be enough species to go round.

What sort of a bird would you assign, for instance, to a walking delegate of the Bricklayers' Union, to a manufacturer of poppet valves, to a trainer of performing seals, to the second camera man of a Film company, to the shop-walker in the hosiery department of Harrod's, to an aviator who has made the first non-stop flight round G. K. Chesterton, or—for the matter of that, to a man who writes essays on the Decay of Falconry?

It is no use deceiving ourselves. There would be a lot of talk and useless discussion . . . a few indignation-meetings . . . possibly one or two letters to the papers . . . but, when the smoke had all cleared away, you, gentle reader, would find yourself saddled with a futile ass of a kestrel that did nothing but eat and sleep, and so should I. I know these committees. They would lump us all together under the heading of "Knaves", and there would be nothing to be done about it.

And even if you drew a goshawk, what would you do with it? Where would you keep it? In your flat? Certainly not in the kitchen, for the cook would soon be complaining that she had all her work cut out looking after her kestrel. Scarcely in the sitting-room, with wives as fussy as they are to-day. The bathroom would seem the only place, and anybody who has dragged himself wearily into the bathroom after a latish night and found a goshawk in it will tell you that there are some things you can do and some that you cannot.

And how about the bird's training? For do not run away with the idea that Falconry consisted simply of inciting a hawk to maltreat birds of other species and just standing by in a negligent attitude while it did it. The matter went far deeper than that. In order to prepare the party of the first part of its assaults on the parties of the second part a careful system of training was required.

"The following", says a learned authority, "is an outline of the process of training hawks."

An outline, mind you. He then proceeds to fill a dozen closely printed pages, a perusal of which has left me with the impression that the only thing you did not have to do was to teach the bird Sanskrit and the use of the trap-drums.

Everything else appears to have been provided for. A good preparatory-school, followed by Eton or Harrow, left the hawk in a condition where four years at the 'Varsity and a final polishing-up at a crammer's would probably render it equipped with a fair education. Though in some cases, where the bird was particularly backward, a private tutor in the holidays was considered advisable.

You can see the trouble this would cause in the home. "Yes, I know our sons are being educated at the Board School," the father of the family would say despairingly to his weeping wife, "but I'm not making a lot of money and you can't have everything. You would insist on sending the goshawk to Winchester. And look at his report, just in this morning. 'Progress only fair. Inclined to be idle. Needs to apply himself more. Has not been a success as a school-prefect.' "

And on top of that there is the matter of diet. "The hawk", says our author, "will easily be induced to feed by drawing a beef-steak over her feet, brushing her legs at the same time with a wing and now and then, as she snaps, slipping a morsel into her mouth." To my mind, this is asking too much of a man. I am of the opinion that a bird which is so finicky about its meals does not deserve them. If ever I am allotted a kestrel, I shall take a strong line. After all, we Wodehouses have our self-respect. I shall be perfectly willing to bring it its beef-steak on a plate with a little watercress and a few fried potatoes: I am even prepared to take it to Claridge's or the Ritz on its birthday: but, having conceded this, I submit that I have done my part. I may be foolishly proud and independent, but I will not brush its legs with raw meat.

But it is unlikely that I shall be called upon to perform this degrading task. Falconry is dead. Apart from all the other causes, the vocabulary of the sport must have destroyed it in time. Your enthusiast can put up with a certain amount of slang in connexion with his favourite game, but there are limits. A pastime inextricably mixed up with words like cere, brail, bewits, creance, frounce, jonk, imping, mew, pannel, ramage, seeling, tiercel, varvels, and yarak could never hope to live. Sporting writers got sick of the thing and refused to report the big meetings. They pointed out to their editors that poor old Nigel ye Scribe had had his head cut off only last Wednesday for saying that the Earl of Balham's peregrine had mantled instead of raking out, and claimed that for family men like themselves the job simply wasn't worth the risk.

So, lacking the support of the Press, Falconry drooped and died. And I, for one, do not care a hoot.

2.   *A Day with the Swattesmore*

WHIT-MONDAY, which to so many means merely one more opportunity of strewing Beauty Spots with paper bags, has a deeper significance for the hunting man. For, if you look in your diary, you will find the following entry:

May 20 (Whit-Monday)—*Fly Swatting Begins.*

Simple words, but how much they imply. What magic memories of past delights they conjure up, what roseate visions of happy days to come.

English poetry is rich in allusions to this king of sports. Every schoolboy is familiar with those lines of Coleridge:

> *It is the Ancient Mariner,*
> *He swatteth one in three.*

These have been taken by some to suggest a slur on the efficiency of the British Merchant Service, but I do not think that Coleridge had any such interpretation in mind.

Mark the word "ancient". "It is the *ancient* Mariner." That is to say, he was past his prime, possibly even of an age when he might have been expected to abandon the sport altogether. Yet, such was the accuracy of eye and suppleness of limb resulting from the clean, fresh life of the open sea that he was still bagging one out of every three—a record which many a younger man would be glad to achieve.

It is Chaucer who is responsible for the old saw:

> *When noone is highe,*
> *Then swatte ye flye,*

which has led some to hold that the proper time for a meet is after lunch. Others, of whom I am one, prefer the after-breakfast theory. It seems to me that a fly which has just

risen from its bed and taken a cold plunge in the milk-jug is
in far better fettle for a sporting run than one which has
spent the morning gorging jam and bacon and wants nothing
more than a quiet nap on the ceiling.

The Swattesmore, the hunt to which I belong, always meets
directly after breakfast. And a jovial gathering it is. Tough
old Admiral Bludyer has his rolled-up copy of *Country Life*,
while young Reggie Bootle carries the lighter and more easily
wielded *Daily Mail*.

There is a good deal of genial chaff and laughter because
some youngster who is new to the game has armed himself
with a patent steel-wire swatter, for it is contrary to all the
etiquette of the chase to use these things. Your true sports-
man would as soon shoot a sitting bird.

Meanwhile Sigsbee, our host's butler—specially engaged
for his round and shiny head, which no fly has ever been
known to resist—has opened the window. There is a hush of
anticipation, and the talk and laughter are stilled. Presently
you hear a little gasp of excitement from some newly joined
member, who has not been at the sport long enough to
acquire the iron self-control on which we of the Swattesmore
pride ourselves. A fine fly is peering in.

This is the crucial moment. Will he be lured in by Sigsbee's
bald head, or will he pursue his original intention of going
down to the potting-shed to breakfast on the dead rat?
Another moment, and he has made his decision. He hurries
in and seats himself on the butler's glistening cupola. Instant-
aneously, Francis, the footman, slams the window. The fly
rockets to the ceiling. "Gone away, sir, thank you, sir," says
Sigsbee respectfully, and with a crashing "Yoicks!" and
"Tally-ho!" the hunt is up.

Ah me! How many wonderful runs that old library has

seen. I remember once a tough old dog fly leading us without a check from ten in the morning till five minutes before lunch.

We found on Sigsbee's head, and a moment later he had made a line across country for the south window. From there he worked round to the bookshelves. Bertie Whistler took a fearful toss over a whatnot, and poor old General Griggs, who is not so keen-sighted as he used to be, came to grief on a sunken art-nouveau footstool.

By the end of a couple of hours only "Binks" Bodger and myself were on the active list. All the rest were nursing bruised shins in the background. At a quarter to one the fly doubled back from the portrait of our host's grandmother, and in trying to intercept him poor "Binks" fell foul of the head of a bearskin rug and had to retire.

A few minutes later I had the good luck to come up with the brute as he rested on a magnificent Corot near the fire-place. I was using a bedroom slipper that day, and it un-fortunately damaged the Corot beyond recognition. But I have my consolation in the superb brush which hangs over my mantelpiece, and the memory of one of the finest runs a swatter ever had.

There are some who claim that fly-swatting is inferior as a sport to the wasping of the English countryside. As one who has had a wide experience of both, I most emphatically deny this. Wasping is all very well in its way, but to try to compare the two is foolish.

Waspers point to the element of danger in their favourite pursuit, some going so far as to say that it really ought to come under the head of big-game hunting.

But I have always maintained that this danger is more imaginary than real. Wasps are not swift thinkers. They do not connect cause and effect. A wasp rarely has the intelli-

gence to discover that the man in the room is responsible
for his troubles, and almost never attacks him. And, even
admitting that a wasp has a sting, which gives the novice a
thrill, who has ever heard of any one barking his shin on a
chair during a wasp hunt?

Wasping is too sedentary for me. You wait till the creature
is sitting waist-high in the jam and then shove him under
with a teaspoon. Is this sport in the sense that fly-swatting
is sport? I do not think so. The excitement of the chase is
simply non-existent. Give me a cracking two-hours' run with
a fly, with plenty of jumps to take, including a grand piano
and a few stiff gate-leg tables. That is the life.

3.   *Prospects for Wambledon*

WHEN I received a letter from a prominent editor asking
me to write a crisp, chatty article on the form of the
more generally fancied contestants for the forthcoming Lawn
Tennis Championships at Wambledon, I confess I was a
little surprised. As one who goes to that bracing seaside
resort every summer to recuperate from the fatigues of the
London Season, I naturally felt a patriotic thrill; but at the
same time I was, as I say, somewhat puzzled. We who love
Wambledon-on-Sea yield to none in our appreciation of its
ozone-filled breezes, its water-supply, its Esplanade, and the
inspiring architecture of its new Assembly Hall, but I should
have thought myself that its tennis was scarcely of a calibre
to excite nation-wide interest.

However, editors know what they are doing. If the public
wishes to hear all about Wambledon tennis, it simply shows—
well, I cannot at the moment think just what it does show,
but it obviously has a significance of some sort.

Tennis at Wambledon is confined mostly to the residents.

Owing to the fact that the words "On Sea" are really justified only twice a day, and that at other times all that meets the pleasure-seeker's eye is a waste of grey mud picked out with broken bottles and dead starfish, we get few visitors. And our isolation is increased by the supine policy of the railway company, which refuses to bring the branch line any nearer than Gluebury Mortimer. It is among the native sons and daughters, then, that we must seek for the winners of the handsome pewter cups so generously presented by Squire Bloomenstein of Wambledon Hall.

Of the Ladies' Singles there is little that one can say. It is always an open event. Matilda Jervis has outgeneralled her rivals by securing a Helen Wills eyeshade. Jane Willoughby, on the other hand, has a larger collection of autographs of tennis celebrities. Muriel Debenham's aunt met Borotra last winter in the South of France. In these circumstances, form is hard to estimate, and I should prefer not to commit myself, but to hasten on to the *bonne-bouche* of the day,

THE MEN'S SINGLES,

which, in the general consensus of Wambledon opinion, lies this year between four men. I allude to George Murgatroyd, Arthur ("Grandpop") Binns, Archibald Twirling, and John Jasper Jones—the last-named our courteous and popular undertaker.

In every event of a sporting nature there is, of course, always the possibility of a dark horse coming along at the last moment to upset the form-book; but to me—and I am supported in the view by the knowledgeable editor of *The Wambledon and West Worsley Intelligencer and Farmer's Gazette*—it seems that when, as Kipling finely says, the tumult and the shouting have died—and I hope those boys will try to be a little quieter this year, especially during the rallies, and, more particularly will refrain from throwing portions of fish at the players—when, I say, the tumult and the shouting have died and the captains and the kings have departed, the handsome pewter cup will be found on one of these four mantelpieces.

Let us, then, concentrate upon this quartette and endeavour, by a minute examination of their methods when in action, to find the answer to the question,

WHO WILL THE VICTOR BE?

A few weeks ago, had I been asked to prognosticate, I should doubtless have confined my observations entirely to the first-named. And this though I am fully alive to the many merits of the other three. Like everybody else in Wambledon, I was dazzled, and I am man enough to admit it. It was early in June that

GEORGE WINSTANLEY MURGATROYD

made his initial appearance on our tennis-court. A graduate of Cambridge University, he had been engaged by Squire Bloomenstein to act as tutor to his son Oscar, a charming but somewhat backward boy; and it is not too much to say that he caused a veritable sensation. I was standing chatting when he arrived, I remember, with little Euphrosyne Burwash, daughter of the well-known contractor and surveyor, and I can testify that she shook like a jelly. At the moment she had been speaking with a good deal of enthusiasm of Ronald Colman; but at the sight of George Murgatroyd the words died on her lips, a strange light came into her eyes, and a bag of pear-drops fell from her nerveless fingers. She was discovered at a late hour that night, seated on the breakwater, reading Elinor Glyn and at intervals uttering little moans.

And I, for one, cannot blame her. No such magnificent vision had ever been seen before in the Wambledon arena. About George's well-modelled shoulders there hung the prismatic scarf of his old college, loosely draped over the throat and blending subtly with the green, orange, and purple blazer of a dining-club to which he had belonged when at the University. He had a lovely tan, and on his snowy trousers and gleaming shoes there was no spot or blemish. Add to this the fact that he carried his racket in a case, and it will readily be seen that here was no ordinary man.

But now, as far as his actual tennis is concerned, the impression created by George Murgatroyd's advent has to a certain extent been blunted by familiarity and the passage of time. That was June. This is July. And in the intervening weeks we have seen George do his stuff, and the scales have fallen from our eyes.

For some days it seemed as though no opposition could live against George Murgatroyd. Nothing like his first serve, the fast one, had ever been seen at Wambledon. It astounded all beholders, dismayed all adversaries. And then, little by little, critics arose to point out that this serve, superb though it was in conception and magnificent as a mere spectacle, had never yet succeeded in getting over the net.

It was a serve that relied entirely on moral suasion. It was a sort of frightfulness. Leaping some feet into the air, George would hurl the ball to the clouds, strike it with hideous violence, and return to earth with a loud grunt. And his pallid opponent, cowering on the other side of the net, was invariably so unnerved by these phenomena that he nearly always failed to return the second serve, which was of a milder nature and more semi-circular, reminiscent rather of the gentle rain after a thunderstorm.

But now, as I say, criticism has done its deadly work. His antagonists of late have been plucking up heart. They cower as before, but rally more swiftly, and recently the second serve has generally been killed. Nevertheless, there always remains the possibility of something practical developing from that first terrific slosh, and it is still felt that George Murgatroyd is a man to be reckoned with. He has the Law of Averages on his side. In the ten years that have passed since he first took up the game he has never yet got that first serve over the net. It may—nay, must—happen soon, and who knows but that it will happen during our annual tournament? Certainly, therefore, we must include George Murgatroyd in our list of Possibles.

We come next to

J. ARTHUR BINNS.

In Arthur Binns we find a player of a very different order. "Grandpop", as he is called—affectionately and at a safe distance—by Wambledon's younger set, is a man of maturer years. Nobody, in fact, knows exactly how old he is. George Murgatroyd's statement that when Julius Caesar landed in England the first thing he saw was Grandpop Binns dancing about on the foreshore, painted bright blue and dressed in a wolf-skin, is, of course, pure persiflage. Personally, I should put Arthur Binns in the early seventies.

His years tell both for and against him. They have of necessity diminished the boyish sprightliness of his nonage, but on the other hand they have given him a wonderful steadiness and poise. He is not a remorseless machine like Archibald Twirling (with whom I shall deal presently), but nothing upsets him. He serves underhand, and has only once been known to volley—in June of the year 1910. His principal asset is his extraordinary knowledge of the ground. And in

Wambledon tournaments to have a familiarity with the terrain is half the battle.

The tennis-court at Wambledon adjoins the Sea-View Hotel, and in his capacity of proprietor of that establishment it falls to Grandpop Binns to look after it and prepare it for the annual Championships. No one, therefore, knows better than he the exact position of the many bumps and hollows which punctuate the smoothness of its surface. Try as we may to prevent them, the village children will play rowdy games all over the court, and it is consequently full of heel-marks. These are thinly filled with loose sand, and a ball which strikes one of them sometimes stops dead and tries to bury itself, sometimes trickles off at a sharp angle. A man who knows the topography of the arena as well as does Arthur Binns must have more than a sporting chance of victory. Local opinion, it is true, is to some extent prejudiced against Grandpop, because he plays in his Sunday trousers and a stiff shirt, and rarely removes the top-hat which is his inseparable companion in his walks abroad: but looks are not everything in tennis, or who could compete with George Murgatroyd?

Let us not, then, dismiss Arthur Binns hastily. He is a distinct possibility. Indeed I, personally, would rank him a shade higher than the third player on my list, his friendly rival,

ARCHIBALD TWIRLING.

Archibald Twirling is a man of method. I have called him a remorseless machine, and that is what he is. In this restless age it is rarely that we find a man who takes one definite line and sticks to it. Archibald Twirling is one of the exceptions. A builder by profession, he builds nothing but bungalows, and each Twirling bungalow is precisely the same as every other Twirling bungalow, even down to the horse-shoe nailed over the front door. He rises at the same hour every day, retires to rest at the same hour every night. He eats one lightly boiled egg every morning for breakfast, and winds the clock up every evening at precisely ten. And so with his tennis. Right from the beginning, Archibald Twirling made up his mind how he proposed to play tennis, and he has never deviated from his chosen course. Whether his opponent be a George Murgatroyd or a Grandpop Binns, his method never varies.

It is Archibald's custom to stand at the back of the court and lob. If his adversary smashes, Archibald lobs. If he tries placing, Archibald still lobs. The longer the game goes on, the higher he lobs, until his antagonist, losing patience or, it may be, forgetting during the long wait for the ball to descend that he is engaged in a game of tennis, omits to return the stroke. Then Archibald shifts his chewing-gum from left to right, or vice versa, calls out the score in a rather melancholy voice, and goes on lobbing.

But Achilles had his heel, and so has Archibald Twirling. For a while, Archibald's progress was one of unalloyed triumph. All Wambledon's best and bravest fell before him. And then one day some shrewd student of the game discovered that he was physically and mentally unable to deal with a back-hand stroke, and now his rivals play sedulously on that fatal weakness.

It is an interesting and a pitiful sight to see Archibald Twirling when a crisis arrives which can only be met by a judicious application of the back-hand. There was a time when he would dive at the ball and try to lob it in the constrained attitude which had been forced upon him. But after lobbing perhaps a hundred balls into the sea, directly at right-angles to the spot where they should have gone, a frozen calm, a sort of dull resignation, seemed to descend on the unhappy man. He has now decided to treat such crises as Acts of God. There is something of the defeatist Russian philosophy in his attitude, a kind of crushed refusal to battle with Fate. To-day, when a ball comes at his back-hand, Archibald just stands and looks at it sadly, in his eye something of that mild reproach which a hat-check boy bestows on a client who tips him with an aspirin tablet.

This vital flaw in his game of necessity diminishes his chances for the Championship, and if it were not for the peculiarly maddening nature of his methods one might rule him out of the race. Persistent lobbing, however, has worn down many a fine player, and we must accord Archibald Twirling at least an outside chance.

We now come to the last name on the list, and it is the name of a dangerous man. There is, indeed, a strong school of thought in the village whose members refuse to hear of anybody but

JOHN JASPER JONES

as the next Wambledon champion. I happen to know that down at the Fisherman and Mackerel odds are being offered on his success which would stun the public.

This Jones has practically everything. As regards service, he is undoubtedly the superior of any of the other entrants. True, he lacks George Murgatroyd's cavalierlike dash and fire, but on the other hand he has frequently been known to get his first serve over the net and on several occasions to place the ball in the right section of his opponent's territory. He does not slash at the ball like George, preferring to throw it a few inches in front of him and then give a sort of stabbing lunge at it. No one who has not played at Wambledon can understand the moral effect of a first serve that gets over the net. One might almost say that it is etiquette not to return it. And, while Jones does not intentionally put any spin on the ball, the irregularities of the ground frequently co-operate with him so happily that he becomes unplayable.

In addition to this, he is, if given plenty of time, a master of the back-hand. I speak a little loosely, perhaps. To be perfectly accurate, John Jasper Jones has never brought off a back-hand shot in his life, and never expects to. But Nature having made him ambidextrous, he has found a way of meeting the situation. Where Archibald Twirling merely stands and sighs, John Jasper Jones acts. If the ball comes to his left, he rapidly shifts the racket to the other hand, and before his startled adversary can brace himself to cope with this new development the sphere is on its way back over the net. I have seen strong men positively paralysed by the manœuvre.

The only flaw in Jones's game is that he serves nothing but foot-faults. This might at first sight seem to reduce his chances of the handsome pewter cup to nil; but the resourceful man has found a way of overcoming this difficulty too. Only a week ago he became engaged to the elderly sister of Bernard Thistleby, our sexton, who is to act as umpire in the tournament: and few of the cognoscenti doubt that, when it comes to the acid test, blood will prove thicker than water. Let me, therefore, come boldly out and state that, after weighing all the pros and cons, my money is on

JOHN JASPER JONES

for the big event.

There is just one other small point to be considered. Old Colonel Warburton will be a spectator, as usual, and something must undoubtedly depend on whether his vocal cords are in shape again or not. At the moment of writing, he is suffering from Clergyman's Sore Throat, induced by a lengthy argument with the driver of a lorry who backed into the left mudguard of his car last Tuesday, and, when last seen, was virtually speechless. If he is still in this condition when the tournament opens, his influence on the fortunes of the contestants will, of course, be neutralized. If, on the other hand, he is in good voice, one cannot say what will happen. It is the Colonel's practice, when watching tennis, to throw his head back from time to time and emit sudden, sharp, hunting noises by way of encouraging the players. You never know when these will occur, and the effect of the suspense on a highly strung performer is frequently to put him right off his stroke. George Murgatroyd is peculiarly susceptible to them, and has been known in the hour of defeat to draw comparisons between the Colonel and the laughing hyena of the Indian jungle. They also affect John Jasper Jones and Archibald Twirling. Should the Colonel have recovered his full voltage by the great day, I should be inclined to transfer my support to Grandpop Binns, whom nothing can disturb. It was Grandpop Binns who, on the famous occasion in 1923 when the soap-boxes which form the foundation of the Grand Stand collapsed, injuring dozens of Wambledon's smartest residents, merely looked over his shoulder with a lack-lustre eye and, observing "Forty-fifteen", proceeded to serve one right over the net into a hole left by Farmer Wilberforce's cow when that animal was pasturing on the court. One cannot afford to ignore nerve like that, for it is nerve that wins championships.

To sum up, let me conclude with those splendid words which are the bed-rock of that love of sport which makes us Englishmen what we are—May the best man win. That the contests will be conducted in the true spirit of British sportsmanship goes without saying. Tea will be provided on the ground and will be followed by a short address from the Vicar in aid of the Church Organ Fund. Should it rain, the Championship will be postponed until next August and a Shove-Ha'penny Tournament in the saloon bar of the Fisherman and Mackerel substituted. As this scarcely comes within the scope of my present article, I will not deal with the prospects for this event, merely contenting myself with recommending as a Safety Bet William Anstruther Simpson, the son and heir of Simpson's Bon Ton Drapery Stores, who, I am told, shoves a superb ha'penny.

NOTE—I find, on re-reading the Editor's letter, that it was the Wimbledon, not the Wambledon, Lawn Tennis Championships with which he wished me to deal; and, strictly speaking, I suppose, I ought to write this article all over again. I am informed, however, that by the time these lines are in print this other meeting will have been concluded; so I will leave things as they stand, merely mentioning that the date of the Wambledon Tournament is August the First and that any of my readers who care to be present will be assured of a warm welcome and hearty English fare. The station bus meets all trains at Gluebury Mortimer, unless it happens to slip the driver's mind, in which case there is a five-miles' walk through delightful scenery. Come one, come all.

Fashionable Weddings
and Smart Divorces

YOU could have knocked me down with a feather the other day when I read in somebody's Etiquette column in one of the papers that the quaint and pretty old custom of having detectives at wedding receptions was dying out. The news broke me all up. Somehow it won't seem like a reception without a detective. But when I had had the thing explained to me, I understood why it was that the man in the flowered waistcoat and large boots had got to go. The growing hideousness of wedding presents has made his passing inevitable. No sane bride or bridegroom will deliberately put obstacles in the way of their removal.

Indeed, the tendency to-day is to encourage in every way the looting of the present-room, and many kleptomaniacs have, as a consequence, at last emerged from the cloud under which their unfortunate failing had placed them. They are now invited everywhere, with the tacit understanding that they do not shirk their merciful work: and I am told that there is no more charming spectacle than that of a young bride smiling encouragement on one of these benefactors as he staggers from the room beneath the weight of a pair of massive ormolu vases, or of a young bridegroom thoughtfully helping some furtive-eyed guest to wedge a silver loving-cup into his overcoat pocket.

Some of the smartest people go even farther and enlist professional aid—a custom that has led to a considerable uplift throughout the Underworld, the members of which are rapidly acquiring tone as the result of being invited to so many fashionable weddings in order to steal the presents.

This growing familiarity with our best families is, I believe, the explanation of that epidemic of the Oxford accent among the larger race-gangs which has recently been something of a puzzle in Scotland Yard.

I am also informed that the rejected suitor has ceased to be a feature of the Society wedding. A few years ago, a bride thought very poorly of herself if she could not muster among her guests half a dozen or more of these: and occasionally this would lead to a pretty and spontaneous effect, as when young Clarence Perkins blew his brains out with one hand while shaking the bride's hand with the other at the Bootle-Bartholomew reception. The incident was the talk of the town for quite a time, and undoubtedly did much to establish the newly married pair in the secure social position they now enjoy.

But too few rejected suitors are like poor Perkins, and the fact is one that we must deplore. It is, perhaps, asking too much of a young man to expect him to commit suicide simply in order to make a wedding reception go off well, but one may at least demand a certain flattering gloom of demeanour. It is the failure of the modern rejected suitor to exhibit this that has led to his exclusion from most weddings nowadays. Not infrequently, indeed, these young fellows would go to the opposite extreme, creating a situation of no little embarrassment. Everybody will remember the painful scene at the Mumbleby-Packsmith ceremony when, just as George Packsmith, of the Leicestershire Packsmiths, was about to reply to the clergyman who had just asked if he had anything to say before sentence was passed on him, a voice from the back of the church was heard to cry in tones of sincere self-congratulation: "There, but for the grace of God, goes Henry Polwhistle Phipps!"

All this goes to show that Fashion does not stand still,

even in the matter of weddings. If the book of etiquette on which you rely to steer you through the difficult waters of social life was published more than two or three years back, you would be wise to secure a more up-to-date edition. Otherwise, some *gaffe* is inevitable.

This is particularly so in the United States of America, where it applies not only to the ordinary wedding-guest but even to the officiating minister. Owing to the ever-growing popularity of divorce and the fact that American divorce laws differ in the various states—so that the dissolution of a marriage is recognized in one but not in another—the canny clergyman now provides himself with a sort of chart or war-map, which he consults at critical moments of the ceremony.

A friend of mine who was an usher at a smart wedding in New York recently, both the parties to which had previously made several false starts in the matrimonial handicap, tells me that when the officiating Bishop addressed the groom with the words "Wilt thou, Rockmetteller, take this Gene-vieve to be thy wedded wife; in sickness and in health, in Pennsylvania and in Massachusetts, in Rhode Island and in Arkansas, in Nevada, Utah, Colorado, Texas and all points west ?" there was not a dry eye in the church.

The practice of holding rehearsals of the actual wedding ceremony is one that is finding increased favour in these days. Originated in America, the custom has many obvious advantages, notably the fact that it enables the bride to lessen the shock to her betrothed by administering her relations to him in small doses instead of in one solid lump. It will generally be found that by the time he has become inured to her various aunts and cousins he is in better shape for bearing up against her Uncle Joe from the Straits Settlements.

But I could write for ever about Weddings. Whether it be the first wedding of a this year's debutante or the latest of

Peggy Joyce, the subject is one that never fails to stir the emotions. What pictures the word conjures up! The bride with her set, determined face. . . . The groom pinching himself in the hope that all this may prove to be merely a fevered dream. . . . The ushers, vainly endeavouring to persuade the distant connexion with the ticket marked "Upper Circle, Z. 19" that she is not entitled to a ring-side seat. . . .

As I say, I could go on writing for ever. And I would, too, were it not that my space is limited and I have not yet, as I promised to do in my title, touched upon the almost equally fascinating subject of Divorce.

Divorce, which may be either an occasional experiment, as in the case of the ordinary citizen, or a hobby, as with Hollywood film stars, is best described as an ingenious device whereby a resolute man with lots of time on his hands may enjoy all the advantages of being a Mormon elder without having to grow a beard and live in Salt Lake City. It is particularly prevalent in America, the land of the Free (or those who intend to be as soon as they have saved up enough to pay the lawyers' bills), where, it has been finely said, every female child grows to womanhood in the assurance that, no matter how humble her station may be, she has a good sporting chance of some day marrying Charlie Chaplin or the Marquis de Falaise de la Foudraye.

In the year 1927 there were 192,037 divorces in the United States of America. In 1929, a bumper year, there were 201,468. But that, it will be remembered, was the year of the great Stock Exchange Panic, and in the following twelve months there was rather a disheartening drop—to 191,591. This was due to the money shortage. Husbands had to be content with giving the old wife a new coat of paint, while wives were forced to make last season's model do for another year. It is confidently predicted that matters will shortly right themselves and Divorce flourish once more at full blast. This is known as the Return of Prosperity.

Divorce in America would appear to vary according to the climate. In the Eastern States the ratio is 147 to every 100,000 persons. As you get into the Mountains and the air becomes more bracing, this rises to 543 in every 100,000. While on the Pacific Coast it goes as high as 656. These figures, however, include the returns from Hollywood, which is scarcely fair.

Impressed by these statistics, we in England have fallen into the error of assuming that America leads the world in the matter of Divorce. This is not the case. Even at the risk of inflaming the Film colony to renewed efforts, we must state the truth—that Japan makes America look like a timid novice in this particular branch of industry. In Japan there are thirty-four divorces per thousand inhabitants, while in the United States there are a mere thirteen. It is but a melancholy consolation to America's patriots that the next competitor in order, Switzerland, only scores three.

This is the sort of revelation which takes all the heart out of an energetic and persevering people. The reason is not far to seek. It lies in the fact that, while certain of the American states are doing all that can be expected of them—we take off our hat to Washington, where there are eleven separate and distinct grounds for divorce—others are simply loafing. In South Carolina, for instance, divorce is actually not permitted, and in many states it cannot be obtained for such perfectly adequate causes as failing to lead back the partner's suit at Bridge, saying "Oh, yeah?", telling last night's dreams at the breakfast-table, and squeezing the toothpaste tube at the wrong end. Naturally, the Japanese, a race which pulls together as one man in every patriotic movement, have little difficulty in keeping ahead.

In England, the outlook is distinctly encouraging. There

was a time within the memory of some of us who are elderly but still well preserved when divorce was mostly confined to the theatre. Except in plays, it was quite a rarity. Then came the King's famous "Wake up, England!" speech, and the old country was stirred from its lethargy. In 1918 the 1917 figures were nearly doubled, yet even that total is less than one-third of the number to-day. We are now doing most creditably, all things considered, with one divorce to every eighty-eight marriages, as compared with one to every ninety-two in the previous year and one in five hundred before the War.

But, even granted that there has been a vast improvement, it is astonishing that Japan's figures should still seem to us a mark to reverence but not to shoot at. When we look about us and see how uniformly repulsive our fellow human beings are, it seems extraordinary that only a mere handful each year take the sensible course of severing relations with them.

The reason, one presumes, is that the expense of divorce is so great. Judges, as a class, display, in the matter of arranging alimony, that reckless generosity which is found only in men who are giving away somebody else's cash. What this country needs is a good medium-priced divorce.

Here again Japan scores. Alimony in Japan is a mere matter of *yen*—a *yen* being, if I remember rightly, about one-three-thousandth of a pound. What it all boils down to is that your Japanese can get divorced half a dozen times a year for about what it would cost him in London to tip the head waiter of a night-club for giving him a table twenty-seven feet from the dancing-floor and directly behind a pillar.

And we have not yet got America's facilities. There was a negress in Kentucky who secured her divorce by the simple process of going to the judge and saying, "Ah done lost ma taste for Ephraim". That is the spirit that wins to success.

Happy Christmas and Merry New Year

WITH the advent of each Christmas a new spirit seems to steal over the community, a spirit of cheerfulness and goodwill. Minor employees of hotels, restaurants, and the like smile at our approach. Our relatives in the country write us long, newsy letters and speculate round the fireside on how much we are good for. Our friends greet us with a merry "Well, Christmas will soon be here!" registering the while a mental vow that, until they know what sort of a present we are going to give them, they are going to be pretty careful.

Everywhere you see it, this genial, Dickensy, peace-and-goodwill spirit.

In these circumstances, it behoves us to be prepared. It is useless to imagine, as every one has done in his more optimistic moments, that people will accept regrets and stories of parcels gone wrong in the post. You worked that, if you remember, in 1925, and it is not a thing that goes well twice.

No, presents must be bought, and the only thing is to try to get off as lightly as possible.

The first rule in buying Christmas presents is to select something shiny. If the chosen object is of leather, the leather must look as if it had been well greased; if of silver, it must gleam with the light that never was on sea or land. This is because the wariest person will often mistake shininess for expensiveness. A shiny pocket-book will get by where a duller gift of twice its value would have been received with sneers.

Books are very popular for this reason. There are very few

things which can look so shiny as a Collected Works of Longfellow, Tennyson, or Wordsworth. Longfellow particularly. I have seen a common house-fly alight on the back of a Christmas Longfellow and slide the whole length of the volume, eventually shooting off with extraordinary velocity and stunning itself against the wall. For this reason a Collected Works will always be a welcome gift. They can be left about the drawing-room in lieu of fly-paper.

They may also be used as mirrors.

Intelligence should be the sheet anchor of the Christmas-present buyer. This and a consideration for others. He should always bear in mind the fact that the recipient will be wanting to pass it on later to somebody as a wedding present. Much misery has been caused in a great number of homes by a want of thought in this matter.

I, myself, am not blameless. I recollect giving as a Christmas present to a friend a rather repellent claret-jug which had been given to me on my birthday by my aunt Charlotte, and which, unknown to me, bore the inscription "With fondest love from C.B.H.". Naturally, this friend gave it to another friend as a wedding present, and the discovery of it among the gifts and the bridegroom's total inability to explain who the fondly-loving C.B.H. was gave the bride an advantage from which he never recovered, and it was only when, a year later, the courts separated the happy pair that he found himself once more in possession of a latch-key.

How different a present was that Smoker's Ideal Comrade which I received on Christmas Day, 1922. It was given me by one of my uncles, and it had everything, including a brass cigar-cutter, which makes smoking distasteful to the right-thinking man. I hesitate, for I am not quite sure of my facts, to make such an accusation, but I rather think the thing included a velvet smoking-cap.

I gave it away in the autumn of 1923 to an old school friend as a wedding present, and thought no more of it. What was my surprise, on Christmas morning, 1924, to receive it back from a distant cousin. I gave it away once again, Christmas, 1925, only to unpack it in my home on the twenty-fourth of December, 1930—this time as the gift of the very uncle who had first given it to me in 1922. The thing had completed full circle, and looked as good as new, though it contained no smoking-cap. It may be that it never had contained a smoking-cap, or possibly the passage of time had wrought more heavily on the velvet than on the brass.

I confess to a not unmanly wave of sentiment when I beheld it once more and thought of all the good men whom it had enabled to give a handsome Christmas present without expense. In a month from now it will be starting out on its travels again, but on a different route, for I am sending it to a friend in Australia, whither, I feel sure, it has never yet penetrated.

In this instance we have watched the career of a Christmas present from start to—I hope—finish. But this is but one of millions. The question of what becomes of Christmas presents must still continue to vex thinking men. Every year a tidal wave of incredibly useless matter bursts upon the country, yet somehow or other it is disposed of long before the first mosquito steps from the West Indian pier into the crate of bananas which is to take it to the Old Country. A proportion of this, no doubt, is kept working after the manner of my Smoker's Ideal Comrade: but the vast majority of Christmas presents simply disappear. My own theory is that they are sold back to the shops, whence they emerge next year in another incarnation.

It is probably true, as I have heard said, that every large

London shop retains a special staff of skilled workmen whose duty it is to transform old Christmas presents into new Christmas presents of a different nature. They receive the combined pocket-book, cigar-case, and handy manicure set and with a few deft touches transform it into Milady's vanity-case. They take the slightly soiled Longfellow and give it a new coat of varnish. The too bright scarf of yesteryear becomes a sweater for the Pekingese.

If I had only known in time of the existence of these men, I could, no doubt, for a small consideration, have got them to make over my aunt's claret-jug into a pair of slippers or a presentation set of the works of Robert Browning.

For that they do exist, I am now convinced. On no other theory is the total disappearance of last year's Christmas presents to be explained. Matter cannot be destroyed. It can only be transformed.

The burden of Christmas-present giving has of late years been sadly increased by the growing sophistication of the modern child. In the brave old days it was possible to give a child almost anything, and to receive in return a very warm gratitude. I can still recall thanking with genuine sincerity a relative whose annual Christmas gift to me consisted of an orange.

In fact, the thought of what the average child expects from you nowadays at Christmas is so saddening that I hurry to skip a week and get into the new year.

It was when I took down my *Encyclopædia Britannica* in order to obtain material for a few thoughtful pages on New Year's Day and its customs that I noticed, not for the first time, a very annoying habit of that great work of reference. I allude to its habit of leaving off just at the point where it has got the reader all agog and excited.

Take, for example, its description of New Year's Day in medieval England.

In those times, it says, it was the practice for the King to "extort gifts from his subjects", adding that in the year 1533 Henry the Eighth collected many thousands of pounds in this manner—being laid a stymie in only one instance, when Bishop Latimer, a man with a good business head, handed him in lieu of cash a copy of the Old Testament with the leaf turned down at Hebrews xiii. 4.

So far, so good. Most interesting. But then, having mentioned that on another occasion the bluff monarch got into the ribs of Cardinal Wolsey to the tune of one hundred and seventeen pounds, seventeen shillings and sixpence, it signs off without a word of explanation, leaving the reader completely mystified. Why one-one-seventeen, seventeen and six? Why the seventeen bob? Why the sixpence?

I have heard two theories advanced. The first, that the King met the Cardinal in a dark alley on his way back from the bank and stood him on his head and lifted the contents of his pockets, does not satisfy me. If Cardinal Wolsey drew a cheque to Self, it would have been for some less eccentric figure, and, knowing that it was New Year's Day and Henry was about, he would certainly not have gone to the bank without an armed escort. It is far more likely that the money changed hands at the conclusion of a merry party in the small hours of the morning. The waiter came round with the bill, and King Henry, after the usual unconvincing fumbling, told him to take it on to the clerical gentleman in the paper cap.

This would explain everything. The bill came to exactly a hundred and seventeen pounds, fifteen shillings. Two bob for the waiter and sixpence for the hat-check girl, and there you are. One can always reason these things out if one tries, but my point is that the *Encyclopædia Britannica* ought not to throw the burden of the brainwork on its readers. Making these silly mysteries is mere verbal horse-play, unworthy of its great reputation.

Another result of consulting the *Encyclopædia* is that my opinion of the ancient Persians has been considerably lowered. I had always looked on them as a sober, responsible people, by no means the kind you would suspect of a distorted sense of humour. And yet, we read, it was their custom to go round on New Year's morning making presents of eggs to their friends—the one day when one simply can't look at an egg. I shall never feel quite the same about the ancient Persians again.

How much more fitting was the attitude of the early Christians. Christians, in the early days of the Church, were, we are told, "expected to spend New Year's Day in quiet meditation". It is a custom which after nearly two thousand years still persists. Visit any of your friends on the morning of January the First, if you are in a condition to do so, and see for yourself. The odds are a hundred to one that you will find him in bed with a vinegar-soaked bandage round his head and the bromo-seltzer bottle by his side, quietly meditating.

Oddly enough, there has always been a great deal of confusion in the public mind as to when exactly New Year's Day really is. What reason have we to suppose that the year begins on January the First? One only, that the ancient Romans said it did. Yes, but what ancient Romans? Probably Horace or somebody at a moment when he was well into his second bottle of Falernian. One can picture the scene . . .

HORACE. Well, boys, Happy New Year, boys.

LUCULLUS (*looking up from the grape which he is cracking with the nutcrackers*). How do you mean, Happy New Year?

HORACE. It's New Year's Day to-morrow. We celebrate it
with masquerades, the making of sacrifices to Janus, and
feasting. Yessir!

MAECENAS. Feasting?

HORACE. Feasting was what I said.

MARCENAS (*thoughtfully*). I believe he's right.

LUCULLUS. I'm sure he's right. Happy New Year.

MAECENAS. Happy New Year.

HORACE. Happy New Year.

VIRGIL. All the same, I could have sworn it came at the time
of the autumnal equinox, on September the twenty-first.

That was because Virgil had been brought up in the school
of thought of the ancient Egyptians, Phoenicians, and Persians.
In Egypt, Phoenicia and Persia the sale of squeakers and
rattles and paper caps was brisk all through September,
culminating on the twenty-first. The medieval Christians, on
the other hand, held their celebrations on the twenty-fifth of
March. The Greeks were broad-minded. Some of them
thought New Year's Day came on December the twenty-first,
while others voted for the twenty-first of June. This was
good for the restaurateurs, who could count on two big nights
in the year, but confusing for the Income Tax authorities,
who never knew when to send in their demands.

One can readily see that this sort of conflict of ideas is
not only bewildering but decidedly inconvenient. It makes it
difficult for a conscientious man to do the right thing. He
starts out simply and straightforwardly enough by taking a
reserved table for the last night in December, prepared to
dance on it should the occasion arise, and there, one would
suppose, the matter would rest.

But mark the sequel. As March approaches, doubts begin
to assail him. "Was I right?" he begins to ask himself.
"Those medieval Christians were shrewd fellows. Who knows

whether they may not have had the correct idea?" The only way he can square his conscience is by going out and lowering himself to the level of the beasts of the field on the night of March the twenty-fourth. And scarcely has the doctor left his bedside next morning with the statement that all he needs is a diet of arrowroot for a week or two, when he starts to brood on the fact that the ancient Phoenicians, who were no fools, were convinced that September the twenty-first was New Year's Day.

By this time he is so uncertain that he feels the only safe course is to hunt up all the data and celebrate every New Year that any nation or collection of people ever invented, with the result that he has only just time to get discharged from the nursing-home by December the thirty-first, the now fashionable date, and join his unthinking friends in their revels. Many a young man, in the springtime of life, has developed cyrrhosis of the liver simply through reading the New Year article in the *Encyclopædia*. My own perusal of it has left me with grave doubts, and I had better be closely watched on the eve of June the twenty-first, as I am beginning to come round to the Greek view.

I have little more to add. If any word of mine enables my readers to approach New Year's Eve in a more thoughtful frame of mind, I shall be amply repaid. If, when throwing celluloid balls at some perfect stranger while endeavouring to sing Auld Lang Syne, you pause for a moment to say to yourself "Even so did the ancient Egyptians do!" or "I bet Henry the Eighth was a whale at this sort of thing!" and, as you break the last remains of the crockery and glassware, you feel a passing pang for the days that are no more, my labours will not have been in vain. I thank you.

Thoughts on the Income Tax

A s I sit in my poverty-stricken home wishing that I could afford the price of a ham-sandwich and looking wistfully at the place where the canary's cage used to be before I had to sell it to pay the last instalment on my income tax, I find myself in thoughtful mood. Neighbours pop their heads in through the door and, withdrawing them softly, whisper to one another, "Don't go in. I think he is sickening for something." But really it is simply that I am in thoughtful mood. A dark suspicion is stealing over me that I have been the victim of sharp practice.

The artist temperament has its advantages and its drawbacks. When the necessity arises for weaving plots and putting one's dreams on paper, such a temperament is obviously so much pure velvet. One could not get on without it. The drawbacks come in when matters of Finance are to the fore. That is when we authors suffer.

It is, for instance, the peculiar characteristic of the artist temperament that it will always disgorge automatically when asked to pay any sum ending with 11s. 3d., 13s. 4d., or 0s. 7½d., provided the demand is made on an official form.

Looking back over the past year, it seems to me that I have received and yielded to far more of these demands than I should have done. I name no names, but I am now convinced that there is somebody in the Inland Revenue Office who knows this weak spot of mine and plays upon it.

Yes, I will name names, too, and let the law of libel do its worst. What happens is this. Mr. Snowden looks in at

Somerset House one morning to fetch a hat he left and finds Mr. Neville Chamberlain sitting with his head between his hands.

"Well, Nev., how's it coming?" asks Mr. Snowden.

"Not so good," replies Mr. Chamberlain. "I feel we're going to be short at the end of the Fiscal Year."

"Don't I know that feeling!" says Mr. Snowden sympathetically. "Hot dog! I suppose you've worked the old Wodehouse gag?"

"What's that?"

"Why, whenever I needed a bit more of the stuff," says Mr. Snowden, "I would just send Wodehouse another demand for £238 13s. 4d."

Mr. Chamberlain starts, and his face brightens.

"Did it work?" he cries eagerly.

"Did it work!" says Mr. Snowden. "It never failed. The man's a perfect ass. You can put the bite on him over and over again."

And so, little by little, and bit by bit, the thing goes on, until one day you see it announced in the papers that Mr. Chamberlain is £2,375,694 9s. 10d. in hand. And practically all of it out of my pocket.

Scarcely British, I think.

Not that I should grudge the money if only I had not the feeling that I was simply chucking it away. Where does it go? What do they do with it? One gets the feeling sometimes that the whole thing is purely malevolent, done in a sort of "You would have an income, would you? All right!" spirit. It would surely be a very simple thing to give the tax-payer some inkling of the use to which his money was put.

I should like to read in the paper some such item as this:

At Bow Street Police Court yesterday, James Brown (36) was sentenced to three months' hard labour for breaking and entering. The magistrate, in congratulating P.C. X.42 on his smart capture, said that he was a credit to Mr. P. G. Wodehouse, who was paying his salary. Mr. Wodehouse, it will be remembered, is the man behind Officer Y.18, who arrested the Bermondsey burglar last week. Mr. Wodehouse is also partly responsible for the upkeep of both His Majesty's land and naval services, and paid for three bricks of the new County Council building. This public-spirited citizen has promised that, if he has a good year next year, he will chip in on the blotting-paper overhead at the Colonial Office.

That would be gratifying. Still more gratifying would it be if the authorities could see their way to some easily recognizable form of reward. Why not something on the lines of the "colours" system at public schools? It would help one in one's business.

"Wodehouse must be doing pretty well," people would say. "I see he's been given his super-tax scarf. If his books are as good as all that, I'll have to buy one of them."

This would appeal to the deepest-rooted of human tendencies, the desire to swank. You would find men with small incomes deliberately falsifying their returns in order to get into the super-tax class. Not much talk about non-balancing budgets then.

And while we are suggesting improvements, why cannot something be done about the method of collection? Why these impersonal forms, these cold documents with all their tactless remarks about Penalties? Why not that direct contact which appeals to all that is warm-hearted in a man? If the Waits can go round singing carols, why cannot the Inland Revenue authorities go round singing Income Tax Demands?

I can see the thing rising to rather ambitious heights of part-singing. Thus:

Scene: The steps leading to the tax-payer's front door.
Enter the Somerset House Glee Party.

Trebles: *God rest you, merry gentlemen,*

Altos: *God rest you, merry gentlemen,*

Tenors: *Merry gentlemen, merry gentlemen,*

Basses: *Merry gentlemen,*

Tenors: *God rest you,*

Altos: *Merry gentlemen,*

Basses: *Merry, merry, merry, merry, merry gentlemen,*

All: *Let nothing you dismay.*

Basses: *Dismay.*

Trebles: *We're needing stacks*

Altos: *Of Income Tax,*

Tenors: *Of Income Tax,*

Basses: *Stacks, Tax, Tax, Stacks, Stacks, Tax, etc.*[1]

Trebles: *God rest you, merry gentlemen,*
        Let nothing you dismay:

All: *We're needing stacks of Income Tax,*
        From Trade (including Mines, Quarries and other
        concerns formerly assessed under Schedule A), Pro-
        fession, or Vocation,

Basses: *(Or Vocation, Or Vocation)*

All: *From Untaxed Interest, Annuities, Annual Payments,*
        Or Dividends,

[1](*Note:* Basses always get perfectly drivelling at about this stage of part-singing. You just have to bear with them. In the present instance they will go on chanting as above for several minutes. Meanwhile, the Trebles have gone back to "God rest you, merry gentlemen", in case you did not hear them the first time, and one of the Tenors, who has not quite recovered from the big Christmas lunch at Somerset House, has switched off into "Love me and the world is mine". Oh, I forgot the altos. They are just singing "Merry, merry, merry" over and over again. All this sort of thing is unavoidable on these occasions.)

Tenors: (*Or Dividends*)

All: *Or Discounts,*

Altos: (*Or Discounts*)

Trebles: (*God rest you, merry, merry, merry,*)

All: *Or From Manorial Dues, Or Ecclesiastical Payments,
etc., formerly assessed under the Rules of No. II of
Schedule A.*

Tenors: (*Schedule A, Schedule A*).

Basses: (*It's a bear! It's a bear! It's a bear!*)

All: *From Dominion and Foreign Securities and Possessions,
From Untaxed Profits or Income Not Falling Under
Any of the Foregoing Heads and not Charged
Under Any Schedule,*

Basses: (*Oh, take me back to that old Kentucky shack—I
said Take me back, for the choo-choo's off to
Alabammy.*)

Tenors: (*Mammy! Mammy!*)

All: *Not forgetting Wife's Untaxed Income Under Any
of the Foregoing Heads, If Not Included Above* . . .

Basses: (*I wanna go! I wanna go!*)

Treble Solo: *We have heard it hinted darkly
     That your leisure you employ
  Drinking cocktails at the Berkeley,
     Having lunch at the Savoy:
So if you will tell us clearly
What's your total income yearly,
We will thank you most sincerely:
     At-a-boy!*

All: *God rest you, merry gentlemen,
  Let nothing you dismay:
We're needing stacks of income tax,
  So pay—pay—pay!*

That would bring us out with our cheque-books. If it

happened to be snowing at the time, so much the better for
the Inland Revenue. It would be a pretty hard-hearted man
who would not add on another shilling or two with Mr.
Chamberlain stamping his feet and blowing on his fingers
outside the front door.

But these are Utopian dreams. What we are dealing with
now is the fact that the Government have got £2,375,694
9s. 10d. of mine, and I want to know what they propose to
do about it.

In America, of course, the thing would be simple. I should
just write and ask for it back. I knew a man in New York
who found, on going over his Income Tax return, that he
had overpaid the Federal Government the sum of $1.50.
He wrote a civil letter, informing them of this, and received
an equally civil reply, in which the Authorities regretted
the error and begged to enclose, as requested, cheque for
$15.00.

My friend returned the cheque, saying that there had been
a mistake, and the Authorities, more apologetic than ever,
sent him another for $150.00. When he returned this cheque
they almost grovelled and enclosed one for $1,500.00.

My friend was content at this point to take his profit and
retire from the game, but I still think that if he had had
the vision and enterprise to carry on he could have cleaned
them out.

A little more of this generous and impulsive spirit is what
we need in this country. Over here the Authorities would
merely have written a curt reply to the first letter, noting
that my friend acknowledged a debt of the sum mentioned
and requesting him to remit cheque by early post. For of
all the hard-boiled, stony-eyed, protruding-chinned descend-
ants of Captain Kidd who ever took the orphan by the scruff

of the neck and rubbed his nose in the mud, these Inland Revenue thugs are the . . .

But I must not allow myself to become bitter. Let me rather control myself with a visible effort and turn to the bright side of the Income Tax.

For it has a bright side. Say what you will against it, the filling up of Schedule D has given us all a delightful indoor game in which old and young can join with equal enjoyment.

See the family clustered round the table. There is Father, with his spectacles on, jotting down some notes on Amortization. There is Mother, leaning over his shoulder and pointing out that by taking Sec. 6248 II and putting it on top of Sub-Sec. 9730 G he can claim immunity from the tax mentioned in Sec. 4587 M. And gathered about them are the children, sucking pencils and working out ways of doing down the super-tax.

"See, papa!" cries little Cyril gleefully. "I note that Gifts (not made as a consideration for service rendered) and money and property acquired under a will or inheritance (but the income derived from money or property received by gift, will or inheritance) are, according to Sub-Sec. 2439, not subject to tax, and the way it looks to me is that you can knock off the price of the bullfinch's birdseed."

And so it goes on, each helping the other, all working together in that perfect harmony which, one had begun to think, would never again be seen in the home.

Nor is this all. Filling in the Income Tax forms has kindled again all the old spirit of love and family affection. How differently nowadays the head of the house regards his wife and children. Many a man who has spent years wondering why on earth he ever linked his lot with a woman whom he has disliked from the moment they stepped out of the Lord Warden Hotel at Dover and a gang of boys and girls who seemed to grow more repulsive every day gratefully revises his views as he scans Schedule D.

His wife may be a nuisance about the home, but she comes out strong when it is a question of Married Man's Exemption. And the children! As the father looks at their hideous faces and reflects that he is entitled to knock off a nice little sum per gargoyle, the austerity of his demeanour softens, and he pats them on the head and talks vaguely about jam for tea.

There is no doubt that the Income Tax, whatever else it has done, has taught the British Father to value his nearest and, so to speak, dearest. It is the first practical step that has been taken against the evil of race-suicide.

Of course, the system is by no means perfect yet. To lump all children together under a single head and have an iron-clad tariff is crude.

It is obviously unfair that the father of a son at whom he can look without wincing and who shows promise of developing into a slow left-hand bowler who can flight the ball and make it dip should be allowed the same compensation as the suffering parent of one of those spectacled boys with rabbit teeth and chronic colds who ask questions all the time in a squeaky, adenoidy voice. Photographs should be submitted and large bonuses granted.

I have seen photographs of myself in my youth which would infallibly have eased the situation for my father, had such a system been in operation forty-odd years ago. "Send this bird a cheque for £115 8s. 11d.," the Authorities would have said, glancing at that one of me in the sailor suit and putting it back hastily in its envelope. "He needs it sorely."

And a week later, after they had had time to think it over properly, my father would have received an additional £63 0s. 4½d. Conscience Money.

Butlers and the Buttled

IF I have a fault as a writer, which is very doubtful, I should say that it was a tendency to devote myself a little too closely to the subject of butlers. Critics have noticed this complex of mine.

"Why is it", they ask, "that Wodehouse writes so much about butlers? There must be some explanation. This great, good man would not do it without some excellent reason."

Well, the fact is, butlers have always fascinated me. As a child, I was brought up on the fringe of the butler belt: as a young man I was a prominent pest at houses where butlers were maintained: to-day I employ butlers: so it might be said that I have never really gone off the butler-standard: and all through the years these men have piqued my imagination. Mystery hangs about them like a nimbus. How do they get that way? What do they really think about? Where do they go on their evenings off? And, if you come right down to it, why are they called butlers? If the word is a corruption of bottlers, it is surely a misnomer. A butler does not bottle. He unbottles.

In these few remarks I shall deal with the best-known representative of the species, the English butler: but scattered about the world there are many other types. In Hollywood, for instance, a butler may be almost anything. The acid test is whether he knows how to look after the swimming-pool. The first one we had was a Japanese, and so magical was his touch with the pool that he was kept on for six months in spite of his habit of addressing my wife as "Dear old pal".

This was all the English he knew, and it seemed a shame to say anything to hurt the feelings of one who so plainly prided himself on being a bit of a linguist.

He was succeeded by a Filipino, who left us to become a prize-fighter. This is the only failing of the Filipino butler. You take your eye off him for a second, and he is out with his manager arranging dates for four-round bouts.

There was one genuine English butler in Hollywood. He worked as a free-lance, hiring himself out for large parties, and this habit of his led to the sudden reform of a visiting New Yorker whose dissipated ways had been occasioning his family no little concern. Going to a party on the night of his arrival, this young man merely felt as he was ushered into the house that his hostess had had the luck to secure a really first-class butler. He liked the fellow's quiet, deferential manner: and thought no more about the matter till he went to another party two nights later and was again shown in by what looked extraordinarily like the same chap. It was noticed during the subsequent festivities that the young guest, usually the life and soul of such gatherings, was strangely silent. He was to be observed standing in a corner, casting thoughtful glances at the man with the cocktail-tray.

On the following evening, invited to a third party, he got no further than the door. One startled look at the servitor who was holding it open for him, and he was off to book railroad accommodation for Battle Creek, where he took a six-weeks' cure before feeling himself justified in leaving. He is now regarded as the chief ornament of a family noted for its rigid views, and in his eyes you will sometimes see the unmistakable look of a man who has passed through some soul-testing experience.

It has always seemed to me one of the most poignant ironies of life that the intellectual poor, who are endowed with the sensibility necessary for the proper appreciation of butlers and the imagination to enjoy them to the full, should be unable to afford them; while the dull and stupid rich, to whom there is no romance in a butler, are never without them. I know a man who has two, one for day, one for night duty; so that at whatever hour you enter his house there is buttling going on at full blast.

This is all wrong. For, hard as it is to be a good butler, it is still harder to be a good butlee. It is not easy to buttle, but it is still more difficult to be buttled to.

As an instance of what I mean, take the case of some acquaintances of mine in Chicago who, after cleaning up rather largely in Wheat, awoke one morning in the midst of the enjoyment of their novel wealth, to find that an English butler had imperceptibly insinuated himself into the home. The discovery left them aghast. Some are born to butlers, others achieve butlers, and others have butlers thrust upon them. My friends belonged to the last class. In the daily recriminations which followed Mergleson's arrival, each of the family denied hotly that he or she had been responsible for his engagement. They came to the conclusion in the end that nobody had engaged him, but that he had just materialized like some noxious vapour given out by their wealth.

At any rate, from the moment of his arrival, happiness took to itself wings. If they had been American song-writers, they would have said that skies were grey and that they had lost the blue bird. Mergleson had been with a Duke, and on the occasions when I dined with these unfortunate people it would have touched a far harder heart than mine to observe the way they cringed before the man. They congealed beneath his cold eye. They quailed at the proximity of his bulging waistcoat. If conversation became for an instant free and unself-conscious, it collapsed at the sound of Mergleson's quiet disapproving "Sherry or Hock, sir?" Sometimes, out of sheer bravado, one of the sons, in the devil-may-care way of youth, would begin a funny story, only to subside half-way through as he heard that short, soft cough behind him—the cough which seemed to say: "Pardon me, but this sort of thing would hardly have done for His Grace."

I forget how it all ended. They could not have shot the man, or I should have seen it in the papers. They could not have given him notice, for they had not the courage. I imagine they talked the thing over, and one night, having made sure that he was asleep, they all packed their suitcases and sneaked away somewhere out West.

I merely mention the affair to prove my point that it is not every man who is capable of being buttled to, and that mere wealth ought not to be permitted to corner the butler market, as it is under the present slipshod conditions of our social life. Over in England, a mere five days' journey from the house of these wretched creatures, there must have been dozens of men to whom Mergleson would have been a comfort and a boon, but who were barred from employing him by their impecuniosity. Some day, no doubt, there will be a sort of Fund or Institution for supplying the deserving poor with butlers. Public examinations will be held periodically, and those who pass them will receive these prizes quite independently of their means.

One can foreshadow without much difficulty some of the questions which would be put to the candidates.

For instance:

(1) What would you do if you were a guest in a big house and you met the butler unexpectedly on the stairs?

Answer (adjudged correct by the examiners):

I should either (a) stare haughtily at the man or (b) say, "Ah, Stimson! I am looking for His Grace, Her Grace, His

Lordship, Her Ladyship, and Colonel Maltravers-Morgan. Have you seen them anywhere?"

(Adjudged incorrect):

I should (a) shuffle my feet; (b) faint; (c) hurl myself over the banisters.

(2) Is familiarity with a butler ever permissible?

Answer (adjudged correct by the examiners):

Certainly. All butlers are interested in racing and the Stock Market. It is perfectly in order to say to a butler: (a) "Oh, Spink, before I forget. Put your dickey on Buttercup for the two o'clock at Ally Pally next Saturday", or (b) "Very unsettled, the market, this afternoon, Spink—very unsettled".

(Adjudged incorrect):

Only in an assumed voice, over the telephone.

(3) What services may a man legitimately demand of a butler?

(Adjudged correct):

(a) The supplying of light for a cigar; (b) a jerk at the collar of one's overcoat just as one has got it on; (c) a corroboration of one's suspicion that the weather is threatening.

(Adjudged incorrect):

None.

It is one of the compensations of increasing age that fear of butlers (that butler-phobia of which Herbert Spencer and other philosophers have written so searchingly) decreases with the passage of the years and eventually, as the hair grows sparser and the figure more abundant, vanishes altogether. But it may be taken as an axiom that a man under the age of twenty-five who says he is not afraid of butlers is lying. In my own case I was well over thirty before I could convince myself, when paying a social call, that the reason the butler looked at me in that cold and distant way was that it was his normal expression when on duty, and that he did not do it because he suspected that I was overdrawn at the bank, had pressed my trousers under the mattress, and was trying to make last year's hat do for another season.

The sting has passed now, but I freely admit that my nonage, that period of life which should be all joy and optimism, was almost completely soured by the feeling that, while we lunched, the butler was registering silent disapproval of the peculiar shape of the back of my head.

But then, those were the days when butlers were butlers. You never met one under sixteen stone, and they all had pale, bulging eyes and tight-lipped mouths. They had never done anything but be butlers, if we except the years when they were training on as second footmen. Since then there has been a war, and it has changed the whole situation. The door is now opened to you by a lissom man in the early thirties. He has sparkling, friendly eyes and an athlete's waist, and when not opening doors he is off playing tennis somewhere. The old majesty which we used to find so oppressive between 1900 and 1910 has given place to a sort of cheery briskness. Formality has disappeared. I know a man whose butler is his old soldier-servant, and his method of receiving the caller is to open the front door about eleven inches, poke his head through and, after surveying the visitor with some suspicion, say in broad Scotch, "Whit d'ye want?" It takes away all that sense of chill and discomfort which one used to feel in one's early twenties when, in a frock-coat which had not been properly pressed, one encountered the Spinks and Merglesons.

It amuses me, when, as sometimes happens, I hear thoughtless people criticizing butlers on the absurd ground that they are useless encumbrances for whose existence there is, in these enlightened days, no excuse. There is one unanswerable retort to these carpers—to wit, abolish butlers, and what would become of the drama? You might just as well expect playwrights to get along without stage telephones. To the dramatist, a butler is indispensable. Eliminate him, and who is to enter rooms at critical moments when, if another word were spoken, the play would end immediately? Who is to fill gaps by coming in with the tea-things, telegrams, the evening paper, and cocktails? Who is to explain the plot of the farce at the rise of the curtain?

Dramatists realize this, and of late years it has been rare to find a butler-less play. In a way, this is a pity. In the old days butlers were confined mostly to Society comedies and farces adapted from the French, which made it very convenient for, directly you saw one come on the stage, you were able to say to yourself, "Ah, so this is a Society comedy or a farce adapted from the French, is it?" and steal away to a musical comedy while there was still time to escape.

Butlers are popular in the motion-picture world, but the writers of scenarios appear to have a sketchy idea of what their actual duties are or how they are dressed. Outside a film drama it is rarely that one sees a butler—in Dundreary whiskers and a zebra-striped waistcoat—announce a visitor and stand listening to the ensuing conversation with his elbows at right-angles to his body and his chin held rigidly on a level with his forehead.

But, after all, the stage has made equally bad mistakes in its time. It used to be a stage tradition that, if ever misfortune hit the home, the butler came forward and offered his employers his savings to help them over the crisis. In real life butlers are almost unbelievably slow to take their cue on such occasions. A friend of mine was telling me of what happened when he was unlucky in some speculations on the Stock Exchange and found himself in the unpleasant position of having to cover by Monday, and nothing to cover with.

A regular theatre-goer, his first act was to ring the bell for his butler.

"Meadowes," he said, "I have had very serious losses in the market."

"Indeed, sir?" said the worthy fellow.

"I hardly know where to turn for the stuff, indeed."

"No, sir?"

"In fact, Meadowes, I am absolutely ruined."

"Very good, sir."

My friend saw that delicate innuendo was useless.

"Meadowes," he said, "if you could see your way to letting me have those savings of yours . . ."

Something like emotion for the first time animated the man's mask-like face.

"No sir, thank you, sir," he said in a quiet, respectful voice. "Not if I know it, sir. And I should like to give a week's notice."

You cannot rely on the drama as a guide when dealing with butlers.

A word about Amusement Parks

To the student of history as he turns the pages of musty chronicles, there is always something very sad and poignant, not to say stark, in the thought that ideas worth millions have so often come to men at a time when the world was not ripe for them, thus preventing them from cashing in and cleaning up on a big scale. One pities these pioneers who with just a spot of luck might so easily have clicked.

In the days of the Spanish Inquisition, for instance, Torquemada, strolling through the dungeons during a matinée performance, came upon one of the humbler members of the executive staff sitting hunched up in a corner. It was plain to him that the fellow was not his usual sunny self and, being a kindly soul who liked to have smiling faces about him, he inquired the reason.

"You look pretty mouldy, Sebastian," said Torquemada. "Why the grouch?"

"It's the business."

"What's wrong with the business?"

"I'll tell you what's wrong with the business," replied the other, as he listlessly heated his pincers at a near-by brazier. "It's going to pot. I'm not kept busy at all nowadays—not what I call busy."

Torquemada said something about the competition of talking films.

"It isn't that," sighed the man.

"Perhaps the supply of heretics is giving out."

"It isn't that, either. The trouble is that our methods are all wrong. What happens, for instance, if we want to put a

fellow on the rack? Why, we go out and chase him and
arrest him and try him and send him to prison and all that,
which all means swelling the overhead, whereas what we
ought to do is change the name of the rack to Stretching
the Stretch or something snappy like that with a sales-appeal
in it and charge a small admission fee, and before you knew
where you were we should be turning them away in hundreds. They'd stand in queues and fight to come in."

Well, you know what Torquemada was like. Cautious.
Ultra-conservative. What was good enough for his grand-
father, he used to say, was good enough for him. He laughed
at the suggestion, and look at the result. Who ever hears of
the Spanish Inquisition nowadays? What dividends does it
pay? It has failed, ruining the shareholders, simply because
it was run without any understanding of the first principles
of human nature.

And, centuries later, along come Blackpool and Margate
and Douglas, Isle of Man, with their Amusement Parks, and
do better business every year.

The men who run these places are students of humanity.
They know—what Torquemada's assistant knew—that what,
if administered gratis, would be a brutal assault becomes,
when you have to pay for it, a source of rollicking enjoyment.

Suppose somebody laid hands on you and put you in a
large round tub. Suppose he then proceeded to send the tub
spinning down an incline so arranged that at intervals of a
few feet it spun round and bumped violently into something,
causing your heart to get all scrambled up with your uvula
and your brain-cells to come unstuck.

What would happen? Next day he would hear from your
solicitor. But at Blackpool you simply love it. Released from
the tub, you run round to the starting-place and jump into
another. And why? Because it costs sixpence a go.

It makes one think when one reads that Blackpool and its sister resorts expect to be fuller than ever this year, and that the proprietors of the Amusement Parks are looking forward to doing record business.

One realizes how sound the heart of the nation must be and how little it will affect this country's potentiality for combat if disarmament schemes reduce the numbers of the regular army. It was Shakespeare's opinion that England would never lie at the proud foot of a conqueror, and if he were alive to-day and spent Bank Holiday at Blackpool he would say the same again. It would be a rash Power that would dare set foot on the soil of a country whose inhabitants can consume hot dogs and iced lemonade, follow them with a few whelks and a jellied eel or two, and then go off and submit smilingly to the Aerial Slide and the Barrel of Bon-homie.

Apart from the sausages, the whelks and the jellied eels, such men have the right stuff in them.

To one who, like myself, has never invented anything, unless you count using a brass paper-fastener to take the place of a missing collar-stud, the most amazing thing about these Amusement Parks is the unfailing way in which those in charge think up new attractions every year.

I picture them as grim, melancholy men with very large heads that stick out at the back. In early life they have had some great disappointment or sorrow, and this has soured them. They hate their fellow-men, and as the law prevents them revenging themselves on mankind in any other way they have to invent attractions. When they devise something that looks as if it were bound to turn the customers into nervous wrecks, they smile twisted smiles and for a moment are happy.

"The trustees got away with all my money during my

minority," says one, "but I have invented an attraction which jerks you up and sideways at the same time and squirts water in your face."

"My wife eloped with the chauffeur in the summer of '24," says another, "but look at the one I've just thought out. You pay sixpence and drop through a trap-door on to a lot of spikes."

"Hot spikes?"

The second speaker is impressed. He realizes now why his companion is known at the club as Big-Brained Benjamin.

"That's an idea. I hadn't thought of that."

"Listen," says the first speaker, his eyes gleaming with a strange, soft light. "Let's amalgamate. Let's jerk them up and sideways and squirt water in their faces, and then drop 'em through a trap-door on to red-hot spikes. Then we'll be able to charge a shilling."

And they go off arm-in-arm and wet the bargain with a vitriol and seltzer.

Before I forget, it seems that the explosion from the neighbourhood of the kitchen which I heard as I was writing my last paragraph was caused by the cook having trouble with the oven.

Apparently the thing exploded, setting her dress on fire, shooting her to the ceiling, and sending her into hysterics.

I cannot conclude this article on a pleasanter note than by offering this idea to the promoters. I look forward to seeing, on my next visit to Blackpool, the great new attraction, The Oven of Joy. It contains all the elements of a genuine Amusement Park success. It makes a lot of noise, it hurls you in the air, and it nearly kills you. I shall be satisfied with a small royalty.

The Small Gambler

1. Roulette

A CLOUDLESS sky, a sea like satin. Air that breathes the fragrance of eternal spring. White walls gleaming in the sunshine; green hills towering to heaven. A Paradise, where falls not hail nor any snow, nor ever wind blows loudly.

And, right in the middle of it all, a wretched little creature in a Homburg hat legging it back to his hotel for more money to spend at the Casino.

It is Nature's comic relief, the SMALL GAMBLER.

If there is one spectacle more than another before which the gods, looking down on the follies of mankind, hesitate, uncertain whether to laugh or to weep, it is the spectacle of the Small Gambler at Monte Carlo trying to make his holiday expenses.

Gambling is so foreign to his nature. Home in England, he is so steady, so level-headed. He lives on a salary which he earns by honest work. Get-rich-quick schemes do not tempt him. He does not dabble in stocks. He does not even follow the races. But, once at Monte Carlo, he is another man.

Curiosity has brought him to Monte Carlo—that and the need for a change. He has not come to gamble. He knows better than that. All he means to do is to stroll into the Casino now and then after dinner, and see if he can't make his expenses. But, if he loses, he will come straight out again. His attitude towards the Tables is going to be one of mild and detached amusement. The poor fish!

Observe him now. He has got that money, and is back again in the Casino. In company with some hundred other human sardines he is straining to keep a position near enough to a roulette-table to enable him to spend the twenty louis for which he went to his hotel just now. His face is flushed. His head is splitting. He has Shop-Assistant's Ankle through standing too long. He has Graeco-Roman Wrestler's Back-ache through wriggling about depositing his stake. He has Goal-keeper's Squint through trying to watch his five-franc piece on red and the whirling ball simultaneously. He is a wreck.

The truth is that to preserve a detached attitude towards the gaming-table at Monte Carlo is impossible. Nobody has ever done it, and nobody ever will.

All that was settled years ago when M. Blanc selected Monte Carlo as the site for his Casino. If you put a Casino where that Casino is, then automatically the place, from the point of view of the ordinary man, becomes all Casino. Only by leaving the neighbourhood can he escape it. It is a case of Get In or Get Out.

Let me explain. At the back of Monte Carlo tower the eternal hills. Now, whatever else you may say about the eternal hills, however you may extol their grandeur and their impressiveness, the basic fact remains that they are hilly; and one of the most deeply rooted instincts of man, if we except a handful of freaks who annually boost themselves over the Alps with sharpened hockey-sticks, is a dislike for walking uphill.

The visitor comes out of his hotel at Monte Carlo of a morning, merry and bright. He takes one look at the eternal hills, and his soul heaves. He turns quickly and goes the other way. This takes him direct to the Casino. That is why it is there.

He has now one last chance. By swerving to the right he can elude the Casino and reach the terrace. But the authorities have allowed for this. Just beyond the terrace they have placed the pigeon-traps, and the visitor, being a pretty decent fellow, is not entertained by the sight of people shooting pigeons. He recoils. A minute later he is up the steps and in front of the Casino again. He hesitates. Then he takes a look over his shoulder at those eternal hills, shudders, and walks in.

Inside the building the authorities display a good deal of sardonic humour. A simulated coyness is their first joke. They know that they want the visitor's money, and they know that they mean to get it, but they make as much fuss about starting in on him as a train does about entering a terminus. Their whole demeanour seems to indicate an agonized uncertainty. It is as if a brigand should pause and ask for guidance from above before going through his victim's pockets.

The visitor goes to a counter on the left, answers questions, is scrutinized, signs his name: goes to a counter on the right, is scrutinized, signs his name again. Then, with the air of men embarking on a great adventure against their better judgment, the authorities give him a card of admission.

But, even now they have not entirely flung away caution. The same solemn farce has to be gone through next day, and the day after that. On the fourth day, wearying of the fun, they let him have an entrance ticket for a month. The wags! They know a week will be his limit.

Ladies and Gentlemen, the Tables! The Temple of Chance. The Plague Spot of Europe.

Here we are, all in amongst the ex-grand dukes and

gorgeously dressed adventuresses, and—and well, anyhow, we ought to be. This is certainly the Casino. No doubt about that. But if there are grand-dukes about, they don't look the part; and, if adventuresses are present, the gorgeous dresses must be at the cleaner's to-day.

To be absolutely frank, this is about the seediest collection of dead-beats into which we have ever been introduced. For the last time, if there is a grand-duke here, let him stand forth.

No answer.

Adventuresses will oblige by identifying themselves in a clear voice.

Dead silence.

Then either we have been shamefully deceived by Monte Carlo novelists, or else these glittering personages must have gone on into the inner rooms. We cannot follow, to make certain, for the entrance fee is two louis, and we are the Small Gambler, to whom two louis means eight stakes. Let us make the best of it, and take a look at the room in which we find ourselves.

There was a music-hall song some years ago, the refrain of which began, "I'm leaving Monte Carlo. I can no longer stay." (To-day's heart-cry!) The first line of the first verse was—

>   *Outside the gay Casino* . . .

The *gay* Casino! It is all the fault of those novelists. They misled the poor fellow, as they have misled thousands more. Their stories conjured up the Casino as a home of jovial revelry—tempered, true, by an occasional suicide, but on the whole distinctly jovial revelry. One pictured the merry cries, the babel of talk, the ringing laughs, and all that, a sort of blend of some gay French *salon* and the "Cottar's Saturday Night".

Well, it is not like that. Imagine the reading-room at the

British Museum, deadly quiet, heated up to about the temperature of the second room in a Turkish bath, and peopled with the inmates of the Chamber of Horrors at Madame Tussaud's come to life. That's the gaming-room at Monte Carlo.

It is a large room, with a parquet floor and some pretty pictures. Against the walls are the settees. In this room, you must understand, except for one or two brief intervals during the day, when the Small Gambler drops off like an exhausted limpet and goes and feeds himself, there are never fewer than a thousand people.

At each of the tables there is seating accommodation for about twenty. For the remainder, the wretched persons with Shop-Assistant's Ankle and Graeco-Roman Wrestler's Backache, there are these settees. On each settee two are comfortable, three a squash. For the tired multitude the management provides four settees.

It is all part of the system which started with those eternal hills. Outside the Casino everything forces you inside. Inside everything forces you to the tables. And, once you are at the tables, human nature does the rest.

This is the reason for the shortage of seats. The idea is to make the Small Gambler so uncomfortable that he loses all that calm detachment of his, and has to gamble in order to make himself to endure his surroundings—just as in a smoky railway-carriage he would light a cigar to keep himself from suffocating.

The sight of his companions does nothing to alleviate his discomfort. I do not wish to give offence or to seem even for a moment to appear to be in danger of saying anything remotely personal, but why is it that five out of ten of the denizens of the Monte Carlo Casino are so totally unlike anything on earth?

I know the authorities are capable of going to infinite

trouble to harass the Small Gambler, but I cannot believe that they hire these extraordinary people to sit there, just to worry him. And yet it may be so.

The fact remains that the sight of them puts the last touch to the Small Gambler's demoralization. Two minutes later, with set teeth and a damp brow, he is watching the wheel rotate. He is no longer calm and detached. No more does he look on with mild amusement. His five-franc piece is on the red, and his soul is a sort of seething cauldron in which dance the following thoughts:

(*a*) Shall I win?

(*b*) Black turned up last spin, so red ought to this. On the other hand, black may be in for a run.

(*c*) Suppose I win, and the croupier collars my doubloon!

(*d*) Suppose I win, and the croupier pays up like a man, and then that freak in front of me with a face like a walnut and a mouth like a scar pinches my winnings!

(*e*) How shall I prove they're mine?

(*f*) He's much nearer the table than I am. He could grab them in a second.

(*g*) I've heard of that sort of thing. It's always being done.

(*h*) I wish I hadn't come.

By this time he has worked himself up into such a state of mind with respect to the walnut-faced man that it is almost a relief when black turns up and he loses.

As a matter of fact, his suspicions were quite unjust—a face like a walnut may cover an honest heart. Stake-grabbing does happen occasionally at Monte Carlo, but it is so rare that the Small Gambler need not worry himself about it. He will find plenty else to worry about. The management will not stint him in this respect.

Another thing that is singularly rare at the Casino is Trouble. Frequently one sees men snarling and gabbling at each other for a few seconds, and then subsiding into grunt-punctuated silence, but a genuine fracas is almost unknown.

When it does happen, the authorities handle it in masterly fashion. Plain-clothes detectives spring up from nowhere, surround the offender, edge him away down the room, and bring him to anchor in a small apartment off the main entrance. Here everybody talks at once, and finally the trouble-merchant is persuaded to leave the Casino. He is never allowed in again. Lucky fellow! That sort of thing never happens to the Small Gambler.

It is a curious existence, the Small Gambler's, unintelligible to the regular habitué of Monte Carlo. He who might be expected to haunt the tables incessantly seldom goes near them. At one time he too may have been a Small Gambler, but he has got over it now, and to him Monte Carlo is simply a place where there is always sunshine and always plenty to do. He is there for the winter, and he settles down to a regular life. He golfs, motors, yachts, and would be horrified at the idea of stifling himself in the Casino in the daytime.

But the Small Gambler is differently situated. He is not there for the winter. A fortnight is the limit he has fixed for his stay, and it is improbable that, once back in England, he will return for years, if at all.

It is now or never with him. Once he has taken the plunge, he eats, drinks and sleeps small gambling. He collects mascots. He talks Casino at meals to other Small Gamblers. He avoids the Café de Paris, the Carlton and the Austria, for these things would keep him up late, and militate against an early entrance next morning at the Casino.

A curious existence. One pictures him as a sort of fakir, one of those Indians who, doubtless from the best motives, spend their time hanging from a beam over a smouldering fire. While the fever lasts, he is just as effectually cut off from real life, and almost as uncomfortable.

My heart bleeds for the Small Gambler. We left him, if you recollect, wedged into the crowd, five francs to the bad, flushed and feverish. Nothing can save him now. He has lost money. He has a deficit to make up. From now on he will spend all day and every day at the tables, trailing that deficit like a bloodhound.

There will be moments when he will have it almost within his grasp. Then it will elude him again. And the longer it eludes him, the longer it will grow, until in the end he will have abandoned altogether his first happy dream of making his expenses, and will consider himself lucky if he can get all square again before the end of his visit.

But he will not. He cannot. That is the tragedy of the Small Gambler. To win at the tables needs dash, and the Small Gambler has no dash. He is trying to do the whole trip, fare included, on a fixed sum, and he becomes of necessity a piker, or, if you prefer it, a tin-horn sport, or one subject to cold feet. In other words, he is crippled by the necessity of having to economize. He cannot take risks.

He tries to gamble prudently.

He tries to treat a lunatic ball as a reasonable human being.

His attitude towards it is that of one arguing with a friend. "You've turned up black six times running," he seems to say. "You must be sick of it now, surely. The sheer monotony will make you want a change." And the ball fetches up at black for the seventh time.

The Small Gambler cannot rid himself of this feeling that what is monotonous to him must be monotonous to the ball. In theory he knows all about runs, but he cannot adjust his mind to the possibility of them in practice. To leave his

stake on red or black when he has won, on the chance of
its doubling and doubling, is physically beyond him.

The even chances are the Small Gambler's hunting-ground.
Red and black: odd and even: over eighteen and under: he
keeps to these; and his ineradicable fear of having his winnings
stolen makes him confine his operations to the side of the
table nearest which he happens to be standing.

To stand in the second row of humanity on the *rouge-
impair-manque* side, and fling a coin across the table on to
even or black is not for him. It is too like casting his bread
upon the waters. It may return to him, but he cannot help
feeling that those appalling-looking cut-throats over the way
will scoop it up before he can utter a cry of remonstrance.

And even if they refrain, he will have to stretch forward
to get his money, which means knocking the hat of the
woman in front of him—a feat which after her last snarl of
disapproval he simply has not the nerve to attempt. And
this is a man who, home in England, knew no fear: who
conducted himself in business crises more like a level-headed
lion of the jungle than anything else.

Sometimes he will play on the two-to-one chances, the
three columns and the first, second and third dozens. But
how shall the Ethiopian change his skin, the leopard his
spots, or the Small Gambler his timidity? *He* does not intend
to plunge wildly on a two-to-one chance. He hedges. He
places a coin on the first dozen, and another on the third,
thus giving himself two chances out of three. If the first
dozen turns up, he loses one coin and wins two. If the third
dozen turns up, he wins two and loses one. If the second
dozen turns up, the world grows suddenly cold and black.
And if the ball, which can do everything except laugh, pops
into zero, he feels as if he had been kicked in the face. This
last tragedy generally drives him back to the colours again,

where zero can do him no more harm than to put his stakes temporarily in prison.

And so he goes on, losing, winning, losing again, drawing level again, then falling definitely behind once more and staying there. He has no chance. All the time he plays with one eye on failure, with searchings of the heart, knowing that it is idiotic of him to gamble at all, and knowing also that it is still more idiotic if he does gamble not to give himself a chance of doing the thing thoroughly.

There is no hope for him. The Goddess of Luck may treat Reckless Rupert shamefully, but she does occasionally smile on him. Cautious Cuthbert simply disgusts her, and she scratches him off her visiting-list from the start.

He is beaten before he begins. His friends ought never to have allowed him to go to Monte Carlo at all.

But then, Monte Carlo is a place to which everybody goes once in his life. It is the one spot in the world where a man may get something for nothing. You are bound to catch its fascination like measles and, also like measles, you are not likely to catch it more than once.

The place is a sort of Purgatory, where the prudent man is purged of that minimum of foolishness of which he has not been able to rid himself in any other way. Until he has actually been to Monte Carlo, he retains, in spite of himself, a secret belief that, if some day he did happen to go, he would make money, that he would bring to the tables the same strong intelligence and self-restraint which have made him so universally respected in—well, wherever he happens to be universally respected.

And then comes the last phase.

The patient's recovery is curiously sudden.

One moment he is losing his money as if it were his settled job in life, his brain whirling with the visions of wiring to his bank for vast overdrafts and winning huge sums at the eleventh hour; the next, the fever has left him, suddenly in a flash he realizes that he has worked harder at this imbecile game than he ever worked in his London office—that he has been paying good money simply to stand at a crowded table and get a shocking headache.

A restful calm steals over him. He is cured. And the convalescent, paying his hotel bill with the broken remnants of his little capital, grasps his return ticket and climbs happily into the Calais express. The great company of Small Gamblers has lost a member.

2. *Chemin de Fer*

I AM writing these words in my hotel bedroom at the delightful French seaside resort, Le Touquet. The hour is two of a fine summer morning, and the man in the next room is hammering peevishly on the wall. The noise of my typewriter apparently keeps him awake. Serve him right. He ought to be down at the Casino, whence I have just returned, losing his money like an officer and a gentleman. He ought to be ashamed of wanting to waste in hoggish slumber the hours that might be devoted to disciplining his soul and forming his character in the Salle de Baccarat.

For there is no doubt about it, the game of *Chemin de Fer* acts on the soul like catnip on a cat. Whether you win or lose, it takes the soul and makes it jump through hoops, purging it of its dross and giving a new meaning to life.

Take my own case, for example. I have just come home on the Casino bus (on which I set out so bravely a few hours back like some aristocrat of the old *régime* on his tumbril) a loser, after feverish fluctuations of fortune, of the equivalent of five pounds: and upon me there has descended a great solemnity—not exactly a divine despair, but rather a consciousness that life is stern and earnest. I have given up the game, of course, for ever, just as I gave up golf this afternoon after missing that putt on the eighteenth green: but I am a better, finer man for having played it. I feel now that I have definitely put my careless youth behind me, and tomorrow I start shaping out a new life and trying to make a mark in the world.

Losing at Roulette never makes me feel like this. In my preceding article I have, I think, shown up Losing at Roulette for what it is—a mug's game. I flatter myself that I have exposed pretty thoroughly its lack of attractiveness as an indoor sport. But losing at *chemin de fer* is somehow different. It may be that your neighbours at the Le Touquet tables have a winsomeness lacking in those who congest the "kitchen" at Monte Carlo. All I know is that my motto is "Millions for Le Touquet, but not a cent for M. Blanc". If I am to be parted from my little bit of stuff, let it be by the man in faultless evening dress.

But to get back to what I was saying about my soul. Where was I? Oh, yes. My soul is in absolutely mid-season form—right in high and doing its fifty m.p.h. I am now a man with a serious purpose. I have done with frivolities. To-morrow I begin reading good books and being kind to the poor. That is how losing at chemmy inevitably takes the man of sensibility, and that is why I would say to every young man starting out in life: "Young man, do not hesitate. The Casino is half a mile down the road, to the right as you leave the hotel. Grab all the loose change you can lay your hands on, hop on to the bus, and go and have a pop at it. And keep on popping till you are down to your last five-franc counter. Then, if you cannot persuade the management to cash a cheque and there is no one about who looks good for a touch, come home, my boy, and may an older man's blessing help you to shape that new career which will automatically open before you." If I had my way, there should not be a youth in our fair country who had not been skinned to the bone at this game of games.

It is a debatable point, however, whether the soul does not expand even more gloriously under the stimulus of winning at *chemin de fer*. There is an almost holy satisfaction in changing your counters at five in the morning and coming back to the hotel laden down with wealth for which you have not had to work. Moralists may talk of the joys of receiving an honest wage for honest labour, but these cannot be compared with those which come from repeatedly standing pat on a five and seeing the banker floundering miserably with three wretched court cards. A general winning a great battle may feel a faint shadow of this emotion, and a sort of suggestion of it possibly came to Milton when he wrote "Finis" at the end of *Paradise Lost*, but I can think of no other parallels.

At such a moment you feel not only clever but curiously good, as if you had done some noble work for humanity and were about to receive the thanks of a grateful nation. You thrill with a universal benevolence. You give the croupier twenty francs for himself with a sunny smile and, if you knew the French for lumbago, would ask him how his was. Also, if they were all well at home and how are his little daughter's teeth straightening out. You feel, in fact, rather like St. Francis of Assisi on one of his best days and rather like Napoleon reaching for the crown at his coronation.

Unfortunately, by one of those curious natural laws which operate we know not why, the drawback is that you only win the first time you try your hand at the game, knowing nothing about it. How well I remember my own initiation, that evening when a kindly friend led me to the table and I sat blushfully at his side wondering what it was all about.

The ritual seemed meaningless to me. Fair women and brave men clustered round the board. A stern-faced man of military aspect was pushing a sort of large shoe-shaped arrangement to the fellow on my left.

"What do I do now?" I whispered timidly to my friend.

"He gives you two cards," he replied.

I received the two cards.

"What do I do next?" I inquired.

"You ask for another," said my friend, having examined the catch.

I rather questioned the advisability of this. My two cards were a king and a queen, which seemed to me a pretty good bag. Would it not be better to leave well alone?

However, I demanded and received a third card. It was a nine.

"What do I do now?" I asked.

"You win," said my friend.

And, sure enough, the military person snatched up a big, flat sword and a shower of pink counters shot off the blade in my direction. What I had done to deserve this, I could not understand, but it seemed all right as far as the company were concerned, so I decided to let the thing go on, with the result that in twenty minutes I was almost snowed under with counters of all colours.

"What do I do now?" I asked.

"You go home," said my friend.

Which I did.

How different it all is to-day. I know all about it now. I am the man you see on the croupier's left, watching the board with eyes like gimlets, waving aside some upstart further down the table with a curt *"Banco prime!"*, and snapping a chilly *"Carte!"* out of the corner of my mouth. When the bank has swelled to imposing proportions and the fainthearts are running to cover with bad attacks of cold feet (*le poid froid*), whose is that rich voice calling *"Banco!"*? Mine. It is now some years since the sobriquet of The Wolf of Le Touquet was first conferred upon me. Bet-You-A-Franc-Wodehouse is a pretty well-known figure along the French coast these days.

And yet—why, I cannot say—nothing ever goes right with me now. I have tried all the best-known stratagems—sometimes smoking while playing, sometimes sitting with a dead cigar in my mouth; wearing my new evening shoes, wearing my old evening shoes; brushing my hair, such as it is, from left to right, brushing it from right to left, not brushing it at all; crossing my fingers; keeping in my waistcoat pocket the foot of a rabbit shot by moonlight in a churchyard; buying cats made of black wool; and having my horoscope read before leaving England: but nothing seems to work. All round me are callow novices whispering to friends "What do I do now?" and scooping in wealth beyond the dreams of avarice, but I, the expert, get cleaned out every time. It is one of those things you cannot explain, you just have to accept it.

And yet, as I say, I am not grumbling. After all, money is not everything. There are things money cannot buy, and one of them is that wonderful sensation of having passed through the furnace which comes from losing thirty shillings at *chemin de fer*.

How futile and contemptible they seem to you as you rise from the table—all these fools grinning over their petty gains. You feel purified and apart, dignified, above all this silliness.

Clear vision descends upon you. You get a true sense of values.

These wretched gamesters with their winnings.... What does it amount to, after all? At the most a few hundred francs which will go in tips to hotel waiters. That is what they will get out of their evening. Whereas you ... Well, you have got it all mapped out what you are going to do. You are going to start to-morrow studying that Efficiency Course you saw advertised in the magazine. You are going to train yourself so that you will be able to look the Boss in the eye and make him wilt. A year from now, people will be asking your opinion, as an established authority, of the works of Artbashiekeff—or, it may be, Scientific Chicken Farming.

Most probably you will become Prime Minister, and that grinning chump who has just let his bank run on six times will be getting trampled on in the crowd which has collected in Downing Street to cheer beneath the window of No. 10 after your great speech in support of the Anti-Gambling Bill.

At this point in your meditations you suddenly find yourself drifting, as if impelled by some mysterious power, towards the desk in the corner where sits the genial soul who will be delighted to cash a cheque for you....

Ah well! No sense in leaving as early as this. Only half-past four? The shank of the evening, you might say. You can become Prime Minister just as easily if you draw another *mille* and strike a winning streak. A moment later, you are striding back to the tables like a leopard stalking its prey.

"Donnez-moi douze plaques, s'il vous plait," you say in your musical patois to the Changer.

Now, then! Come along! How much in the bank? Fifty louis? It would take more than that to scare you.

"*Banco!*" You can't keep a good man down.

On Ocean Liners

I<small>T</small> was as far back as the year 1904, I recall (giving my tarry trousers a hitch and shifting my quid to the other cheek), that I made my first trip to America. Since then I have crossed the Atlantic Ocean so many times that the exact total of my voyages has escaped me. (It must be an even number, or I should not be here, and I have witnesses to prove that I am, but over there.) And the reason I have brought this subject up is that every time I have taken the journey I have been struck by the same thing. The boat is splendid. The food is fine. The air is bracing. The beds are comfortable. And the stewards, whether they be of the White Star or the Cunard, never fall from that amazingly high standard of helpfulness and civility which makes an English liner-steward one of the noblest of created things. There is just one drawback to ocean travel, and that is the extraordinary hideousness of one's fellow-passengers.

When the Cunard Company decided so abruptly the other day to abandon work on their new 73,000-tonner, the reason given out was that their money had also given out. In my opinion, this was a mere tactful evasion. What really happened was that they had a sudden vision of the sort of people who would be travelling on her, and it just took all the heart out of them.

It seems incredible that in this age of progress steps have not been taken to improve the standard of looks among ocean-travellers. Time after time I have stepped on board, full of optimism and feeling that this trip my fellow-voyagers will be—I do not say human, but at least semi-human. And every time I have staggered back with a hand over my eyes, moaning "No, no!".

You may argue that it is not their fault that they look like that. I say it is. When you see a fat man in a yachting-cap, horn-rimmed spectacles, plus fours, and black and white buckskin shoes, I maintain that there is convincing evidence of premeditation and that the matter should be firmly dealt with by the proper authorities.

Either these people should not be allowed on board at all, or—if it is really necessary to get them out of the country—they should be hurried up the gang-plank under cover of darkness and kept in irons till the end of the voyage. It is no good calling a vessel the World's Wonder-Ship and having Edmond Dulac and Maurice Greiffenhagen do the decorating if you are going to permit these eyesores to wander at large about the decks.

It is not as if you could avoid them. If the weather is rough, they stay below, it is true: but anything like a fine day brings them out in shoals. You would hardly credit the spectacle presented by the A deck of a fashionable liner on a sunny afternoon half-way through the voyage. The B deck is just as bad. And the Boat Deck is, if anything, worse, because you find them up there playing shuffleboard. And if you hide in your stateroom you have got to meet them at meals.

The question of meals on board ship is a very vital one. At the beginning of the trip you go to a steward on the D deck, and he assigns you to a table. And at that table you have got to remain till the finish. And even if you have the good fortune to be herded in with a moderately attractive group, what charm they have is bound to wane after you have lunched and dined with them six successive days.

Take the case of the poor devils who have me at their

table. What happens? On the first day of the voyage I imagine that they look me over in a not unkindly spirit and say to themselves, "Ah! Jolly old Wodehouse, eh? Capital!" The second day, they begin to feel that they have seen me before somewhere and that I am not nearly such an eyeful as they had imagined at first glance. The third day, a sort of nervous irritation floods over them as I sink into my seat and reach for the menu.

By dinner-time on the fourth day they feel that this has been going on for ever, that there never was a time when they were not sitting at a table looking at my beastly face. My bald head gleams in the light of the electric bulbs, and they wish they could hurl something at it. More and more do they resent the vacant stare of my infernal eyes behind their spectacles. The way I eat seems to them proof of a diseased soul.

And all the time I am glowering at them, astounded that even mother-love could have saved them from being drowned in buckets during infancy.

It is the sort of thing that cannot but stand in the way of the Brotherhood of Man.

Something has been done to alleviate this evil by the establishment of Ritz cafés on the larger boats. But this has merely scratched the surface. Even if you do not have to feed with your fellow-passengers, you still see them on deck.

In order that nobody shall be able to say of me that I am merely one of those destructive critics who expose the sore but do not suggest the remedy, I have formulated a scheme which would, I think, go far towards improving conditions on ocean liners.

Already the authorities have seemed to be groping in the right direction. Before you can sail, they insist that you get a passport. And before you can get a passport you have to forward a photograph to the Embassy. But the obvious next step they have not taken. The solution of a crying evil was staring them in the face, but they did not see it. What they should do from now on is to take a firm line and refuse passports to all whose photographs fail to satisfy a Board of Censors specially created to deal with this matter.

This is an age of censorship. When I write my daring sex-play, I have to submit it to Lord Cromer, who starts licking his blue pencil the moment he has opened the envelope. When my motion-picture, *Scarlet Lips*, has been shot, there is Will Hays waiting to blow the whistle if necessary. Why, then, should there not be a censor for ocean travellers?

He would, of course, have to be chosen with a good deal of care. You could not select a man for a post like that hap-hazard. As regards the female passengers, they could safely be left to Mr. C. B. Cochran. But for male travellers the business of sifting would be more difficult. You would have to have someone with intelligence enough to see that it is possible for the masculine face to possess a certain elusive charm which amply compensates for an absence of more conventional good looks.

I myself, for instance, am—strictly speaking—no Ronald Colman. At first sight you might say to yourself that I am just the sort of man the censors would have to take a strong line about right away. But do not be too hasty. Wait a bit. See me first in my new autumn suit with the invisible blue stripe. Suspend judgment till my last lot of collars come from the makers. Ah! you hesitate. Exactly. Mine is a style of beauty that grows on you. It has to have time to get its effect. And there are many more like me. It would be fatal if the Board of Censors were composed of men of hasty and impulsive mind. They would need to be cool, canny persons with educated eyes.

But in the main their work would be simple enough. A rough, working code could be drawn up without much difficulty. Two chins or more, for instance, would automatically disqualify the entrant. Horn-rimmed spectacles would be allowed only if the face were thin. Ears sticking out at right-angles would get a black mark, and would have to be compensated for by singular beauty in the nose or mouth. There would be a standard measurement for foreheads, and it would be easier for a rich man to pass through the eye of a camel than for a gold tooth to win its way across the gang-plank of the *Aquitania*.

It may be that there are objections to such a scheme, of which I know nothing. I merely throw out the suggestion and leave it to the authorities to adopt it or let it go, as they please. But I do say this, that it is either a question of creating some such Board of Censors or abolishing ocean liners altogether. If things are allowed to go on as at present; if small men with thin legs are permitted to roam the decks at will in knickerbockers and stockings; if there is to be no bar to a man with a face like Epstein's Genesis sitting opposite you in the smoking-room; then—and I say it with all the impressiveness at my command—something will snap. Human nature can be pushed just so far.

One of these days, unless something is done, when the *Berengaria* ties up at her slip, those on shore will notice that the scuppers are red and dripping. Headless corpses will dot the settees in the lounge. Mangled remains will be among the features of interest in the saloon. And a few hundred gargoyles will have made their last trip across the Atlantic.

Let the authorities act while there is yet time.

Photographs and Photographers

ONE of the things which most acutely exasperate lovers of justice in this world is the difficulty of fixing responsibility. Too often it happens that, wishing to execrate the originator of some particularly noxious evil, we are baffled for want of evidence. Nobody, for instance, knows who introduced the rabbit into Australia, jazz music into London, or the expression "Sorry you were tr-r-r-r-oubled" into our telephone exchanges. And, similarly, it is impossible to say with any real certainty who it was who discovered photography.

The *Encyclopædia* is guarded on the subject—cautious, evasive. It obviously has a wary eye open for libel actions. "K. W. Sheele" it says "was the first to investigate the darkening action of sunlight on silver chloride." As if we didn't know that! Why, we can remember as if it were yesterday sitting on our nurse's knee and listening with delicious shivers of excitement (and a bit scared, too, if we must confess it) to the story of how K. W. Sheele—Bill, his friends called him—found that when silver chloride was exposed to the action of light beneath water there was dissolved in the fluid a substance which, on the addition of lunar caustic, caused the precipitation of the silver chloride.

"And on applying a solution of ammonia to the blackened chloride, Master George, what do you think was left behind? An insoluble residue of metallic silver!"

"Oo, Nanny!" we used to pipe in our shrill, childish treble. "Now tell us about Jack and the Beanstalk."

All very good as far as it goes. But you cannot possibly

start burning a man in effigy on rambling evidence like that. Granted that K. W. Sheele did fool about with blackened chloride. Admitted that his experiments with the residue of metallic silver won for him the affectionate nickname of The Pest of Ponder's End. How can we say, even then, that it was due to him that a train of events started which culminated last week in our facing a forty-two-centimetre camera with a frozen smile on our lips and rendering ourselves liable to a bill from Captain Kidd's grandson for ten pounds eleven and sixpence?

No. We must be fair. We shall investigate K. W. Sheele's movements and antecedents, but until the report is in we must suspend judgment. All we will say at this point is that, if K. W. Sheele does prove guilty, he will be the object of the concentrated dislike of virtually every civilized man.

Man, we say. Not woman. It is not women on whom the hardships of photography weigh. Women as a sex enjoy being photographed. It is second nature for them, on catching sight of a long-haired man in spectacles diving into a velvet nose-bag, to assume without an instant's hesitation an expression in which sweetness, dignity, kittenishness, soulfulness and spontaneity are so nicely blended that broken sentences of admiration and esteem filter through the velvet in an excited torrent.

Debutantes who have not undergone the ordeal since they were taken in the nude sitting on a cushion at the age of two need as little encouragement as actresses who have played in every failure in the last sixteen seasons. And these devoted women, as everybody knows, will rise at six a.m. and reduce their midday meal to a mere snack in order to crowd their daily dealing with the camera into the twenty-four hours. One eminent member of the profession, indeed, on learning that there was some danger of a shortage of her photographs owing to the growing demand, is said to have sat before the lens without a pause for a period of two days and a night, sustained only by indomitable courage and hourly injections of clear soup from a hypodermic syringe.

How different with Man! For some reason, due probably to his nobler and more spiritual nature, the average man is overcome in the presence of a camera with an embarrassment which would be excessive if he were being arrested for forgery while eloping with somebody else's wife. He tries to cover this with a look of brooding gloom, which the photographer (who, owing to the fact that he makes a lot of money without doing any work for it, is an optimist) will not permit for an instant. The photographer is all for more sweetness and light, and, as a means towards obtaining these, suggests the moistening of the lips with the tip of the tongue.

To a thoughtful man like myself, it is one of the most inexplicable things in our daily life, this pathetic faith which all photographers have in this curious operation. They seem to regard the moistening of the lips with the tip of the tongue as a panacea for all human ills. No mundane sorrow, they appear to think, can stand up against it. I often wonder if they carry the hallucination into their private lives.

It would make a good curtain for an instalment in a romantic serial. The hero is sitting alone in his deserted flat, his head buried in his hands. Life seems ended for him. The future—if there is a future—is black. But, unseen by him, the door has opened, and there has stolen softly in a kind-faced man with a velvet nose-bag tucked under his arm. It is his old school chum, Tom, who runs the fashionable photograph-studio in Bond Street.

Tom places a hand gently on the stricken man's shoulder.

"Cheer up, Ralph," he whispers. "You have had a hard knock, lad, I know. Your wife has run away from you and, what is worse, has done it in the car on which you are still paying monthly instalments. But what of it? The sun is still shining. There are still blue-birds in the world. Moisten the lips with the tip of the tongue, boy, and be your old merry self once more."

No photographer will ever admit that Hamlet and King Lear are to be pitied for their misfortunes. They wilfully omitted to moisten the lips with the tip of the tongue.

I say that it would make a great situation in a story, but it will never be written. Authors will not write about photographers. Search through literature, and where will you find a photographer hero? Butchers have been heroes of novels. So have drapers. So have policemen, prize-fighters, footballers, engineers, cowboys, bespoke tailors and Italian oil-and-colour men, but never a photographer. There is a reason for this.

I look in my glass, dear reader, and what do I see? Nothing so frightfully hot, believe me. The face is slablike, the ears are large and fastened on at right-angles. Above the eyebrows comes a stagnant sea of bald forehead, stretching away into the distance with nothing to relieve it but a few wisps of lonely hair. The nose is blobby, the eyes dull, like those of a fish not in the best of health. A face, in short, taking it for all in all, which should be reserved for the gaze of my nearest and dearest who, through long habit, have got used to it and can see through to the pure white soul beneath. At any rate, a face not to be scattered about at random and come upon suddenly by nervous people and invalids.

And yet, just because I am an author, I have to keep on being photographed. It is the fault of publishers and editors, of course, really, but it is the photographer who comes in for the author's hate.

Something has got to be done about this practice of publishing authors' photographs. We have to submit to it, because editors and publishers insist. They have an extraordinary superstition that it helps an author's sales. The idea is that the public sees the photograph, pauses spell-bound for an instant, and then with a cry of ecstasy rushes off to the book-shop and buys copy after copy of the gargoyle's latest novel.

Of course, in practice, it works out just the other way. People read a review of an author's book and are told that it throbs with a passion so intense as almost to be painful, and are on the point of digging seven-and-sixpence out of their child's money-box to secure a copy, when their eyes fall on the man's photograph at the side of the review, and they find that he has a face like a rabbit and wears spectacles and a low collar. And this man is the man who is said to have laid bare the soul of a woman as with a scalpel.

Naturally their faith is shaken. They feel that a man like that cannot possibly know anything about Woman or any other subject except where to go for a vegetarian lunch, and the next moment they have put down the hair-pin and the child is seven-and-six in hand and the author his ten per cent. or whatever it is to the bad. And all because of a photograph. In virtually every case where a photographer is found mysteriously murdered, the first thing the Big Four at Scotland Yard do is to hold a round-up of the novelists and short-story writers in the neighbourhood.

For the ordinary man, the recent introduction of high-art methods into photography has done much to diminish the unpleasantness of the operation. In the old days of crude and direct posing, there was no escape for the sitter. He had to stand up, backed by a rustic stile and a flabby canvas sheet covered with exotic trees, glaring straight into the camera. To prevent any eleventh-hour retreat, a sort of spiky thing was shoved firmly into the back of his head leaving him with the choice of being taken as he stood or having an inch of steel jabbed into his skull. Modern methods have changed all that.

There are no photographs nowadays. Only "camera portraits" and "lens impressions". The full face has been abolished. The ideal of the present-day photographer is to eliminate the sitter as far as possible and concentrate on a general cloudy effect. I have in my possession two studies of my Uncle Theodore—one taken in the early 'nineties, the other in the present year. The first shows him, evidently in pain, staring before him with a fixed expression. In his right hand he grasps a scroll. His left rests on a moss-covered wall. Two sea-gulls are flying against a stormy sky.

As a likeness, it is almost brutally exact. My uncle stands for ever condemned as the wearer of a made-up tie.

The second is different in every respect. Not only has the sitter been taken in the popular modern "one-twentieth face", showing only the back of the head, the left ear and what is either a pimple or a flaw in the print, but the whole thing is plunged in the deepest shadow. It is as if my uncle had been surprised by the camera while chasing a black cat in his coal-cellar on a moonlight night. There is no question as to which of the two makes the more attractive picture. My family resemble me in that respect. The less you see of us, the better we look.

Little more remains to be said on this absorbing subject. If I have seemed to write in a jaundiced and condemnatory spirit of photographers, let me end on a note of kindly approval. Say what we may against photographs, they remain—I speak now of the stiff, cabinet size—the best paper-cutters in existence. The big, limp, artistic ones, if torn and properly doubled up, make admirable wedges for stopping windows from rattling. And let us never forget that if there were no photographs there would be no photograph-frames: and where would we turn then for an adequate yet inexpensive birthday, wedding, or Yule-tide gift for our wide circle of friends?